# AN INTRODUCTION TO AMATEUR COMMUNICATIONS SATELLITES

by

## A. Pickard

GW00568193

**BERNARD BABANI (publishing) LTD
THE GRAMPIANS
SHEPHERDS BUSH ROAD
LONDON W6 7NF
ENGLAND**

# Please Note

Although every care has been taken with the production of this book to ensure that any projects, designs, modifications and/or programs etc. contained herewith, operate in a correct and safe manner and also that any components specified are normally available in Great Britain, the Publishers do not accept responsibility in any way for the failure, including fault in design, of any project, design, modification or program to work correctly or to cause damage to any other equipment that it may be connected to or used in conjunction with, or in respect of any other damage or injury that may be so caused, nor do the Publishers accept responsibility in any way for the failure to obtain specified components.

Notice is also given that if equipment that is still under warranty is modified in any way or used or connected with home-built equipment then that warranty may be void.

First Published — November 1990

British Library Cataloguing in Publication Data
Pickard, A.
    An introduction to amateur communications satellites.
    1. Amateur radio communication. Use of
    communication satellites
    I. Title
    621.38416

    ISBN 0 85934 235 2

Printed and bound in Great Britain by Cox & Wyman Ltd, Reading

# Preface

Satellite communications play a very large role in our information technology based society. Although they can not be seen with the naked eye people are perhaps more aware of their existence now, due partly to the increasing popularity of satellite television and the appearance of small satellite dishes on house and office rooftops.

Satellites in their hundreds orbit the earth and come in a variety of shapes and sizes. To attempt to cover the full range of the subject in descriptive and technical terms in one book is impossible. An introductory book such as this one attempts to provide an outline of the subject, but by confining itself to the amateur satellites, enables the basic principles of the hardware (mechanical and electronic) to be explored and with many examples of technical detail hopefully goes beyond the drier descriptive treatment into practical examples. This includes important details such as operating frequency, life expectancy, orbital path and so on.

The overall objective of the book is to describe satellites available to the hobbyist, whether a home or school user, then to detail some typical receiving systems and system approaches. There are currently several organisations, especially in the educational sector, dealing with satellite tracking. There are also a large number of firms which deal with the hobbyist market. In short, there is already a rather large and complex infrastructure in existence which the newcomer may find difficult to penetrate. One of the aims of this book is to alleviate this.

Satellite tracking and the reception (and transmission) of signals is a fascinating and growing (and also significantly established) part of microelectronic and radio technology as well as being educational in other spheres. It is therefore worth taking the trouble to establish effective methods of obtaining the most useful information which is currently available from a number of sources. This book will therefore attempt to explain system details and provide appropriate references to organisations and suppliers. It must be noted however, that suppliers products, availability and prices are subject to change at short notice although the information given should assist potential purchasers, constructors and users.

The reasons for wishing to set up a satellite receiving system at home or in a school/college department may vary. In the case of weather satellites the reasons may be a genuine interest in the study of weather conditions or simply the fascination of 'taking pictures' at 100 km altitudes, however poor the resolution! A further reason could be the sense of satisfaction in receiving weather pictures independently of the BBC/ITV and putting the home computer to yet another good use (this will appeal to the many radio amateurs who already use their machines as tools for receiving RTTY, etc.).

Equipment within the hobbyist budget is discussed and is partly described in detail. As always, suppliers may change product specification, availability, prices, etc., but I consider it to be useful to describe actual products which are or have recently been available. A main reason for doing this is so that readers can see the potential and possibilities for connecting up suitable satellite receiving equipment for use with their home computer.

I hope readers will share my fascination for this subject which can involve the use of very sophisticated space vehicle control techniques and also electronics and software which are within the reach of the 'home user'. Few, if any, individuals can afford to launch their own satellite or to set up a full scale ground station. They can, however, with a modest outlay and patience achieve some very satisfying and rewarding results from received signals, whether in the form of telemetry data or picture information.

Being able to predict the passage of, for example, a UoSAT craft overhead and then receive 'live' data from it and produce processed results on screen is a very exciting and worthwhile experience.

I would like to thank three people in particular who have provided substantial assistance in the preparation of this book. They are firstly, David Duff, Research Manager of Unilab Ltd who kindly loaned me UoSAT and NOAA receiving and decoding systems and also comprehensive documentation. Secondly, Craig Underwood, a Research Fellow at the

University of Surrey who has been most helpful in providing up to date information on UoSATs. Last, but not least, Ron Broadbent of AMSAT-UK has been very helpful by pointing out a number of inaccuracies, particularly where 'dead' satellites are concerned. He has also allowed the reproduction of various tables from AMSAT-UK publications.

*Alan Pickard*

# DEDICATION

To Cheryl, Lucy and Alice

# Contents

# Acknowledgements

The Author and Publishers wish to acknowledge with thanks, the following organisations for their assistance and co-operation in allowing certain figures and material to be used in the preparation of this book.

Amsat - UK

P.W. Publishing Ltd

University of Surrey
(Department of Electronic and Electrical Engineering)

# Chapter 1

# DEFINING A SATELLITE

A definition of a satellite is a useful starting point and will help in understanding how diversified communications satellites are. This first chapter is also intended to provide an insight into the various complex systems which are involved in satellite communications.

The term satellite to many people is assumed to refer to a man-made device which orbits the earth and requires a large dish aerial and sophisticated tracking and control equipment, such as that which is installed in the large radio receiving station at Goonhilly in Cornwall.

A typical dictionary definition of the word satellite would be as follows. 'A small or secondary heavenly body such as a spacecraft, launched by a rocket into space and put into orbit round the earth.' (For the linguistically minded the word has Latin origins, i.e. satelles, satellitis — an attendant.)

For our purposes, the term satellite refers to a body which orbits another body and could be considered to be a natural satellite (e.g. moon around the earth, etc.), or a man-made artefact or artificial satellite which is placed in orbit around the earth.

Any object then, whether a moon, a piece of meteoric debris, a man-made object or resultant debris can be considered to be a satellite orbiting around the earth.

A satellite must be under the influence of the earth's gravitational force.

A simple representation of the physical appearance of a satellite craft is shown in Figure 1.1.

The main body contains equipment such as engines, fuel tanks and motors for positioning. Radio and computer equipment maintains communication with the ground station, i.e. on earth. Other basic features are special purpose aerials and a solar array for the acquisition of electrical energy via the sun.

Recently, however, the growth of satellite television has resulted in many people associating satellites with fairly

1

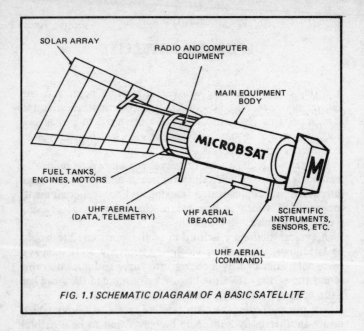

SOLAR ARRAY

RADIO AND COMPUTER
EQUIPMENT

MAIN EQUIPMENT
BODY

MICROBSAT

M

FUEL TANKS,
ENGINES, MOTORS

UHF AERIAL
(DATA, TELEMETRY)

VHF AERIAL
(BEACON)

SCIENTIFIC
INSTRUMENTS,
SENSORS, ETC.

UHF AERIAL
(COMMAND)

*FIG. 1.1 SCHEMATIC DIAGRAM OF A BASIC SATELLITE*

expensive 'domestic' dish aerials and receivers costing around
£1000.

These somewhat prohibitive costs along with the microwave frequencies requirement can be a discouragement to
potential satellite hobbyists.

The subject of satellite communications is very wide rang-
ing and can appear complex, but perhaps we could clarify the
situation at this stage, to enable us to look in some detail at a
more 'user friendly' level.

It should perhaps be realised that not all satellites operate
on radio frequencies in the GHz range (thousands of MHz).
UHF (hundreds of MHz) and even VHF (tens of MHz) frequencies are employed. Relatively simple receiver/decoder
systems can be purchased for around £150 'off the shelf',
or even less for the dedicated home constructor. (More
details of this later.) It follows then, that at UHF or VHF
frequencies the required aerial does not have to be expensive,

unlike a microwave dish aerial, but may be a simple dipole arrangement.

## Microelectronics and Telecommunications

Before going into details of particular satellite systems, we should be aware that many telecommunications principles are employed in satellite communications, and also micro-electronics systems utilising digital techniques and of course microprocessors. An understanding of the makeup of the basic satellite is useful, even though the user may only be concerned with the data being transmitted and of course being received and processed.

The diagram of Figure 1.2 complements the pictorial diagram of Figure 1.1, and as can be imagined, represents a number of engineering systems and sub-systems costing several thousands of pounds and representing many, many man-hours of design, research and construction work.

One of the fascinations of receiving data from a satellite is that you are in your small way participating in advanced, sophisticated and very costly technology.

## The Structure of a Satellite System

This may be grouped into the following disciplines:

1. Basic engineering
2. Science (physics, etc.)
3. Astronomy
4. Navigation (including geography)
5. Telecommunications engineering (including microelectronics and microprocessors)
6. Mathematics (applied to all of the above).

As we are more interested in the information received from a satellite, we will consider satellite systems predominantly from a telecommunications and electronics angle and therefore more detail in this area will be covered.

A true communications satellite operates in the Gigahertz frequency range and carries maybe hundreds of traffic channels (e.g. telephone, data) which are operated on a commercial basis.

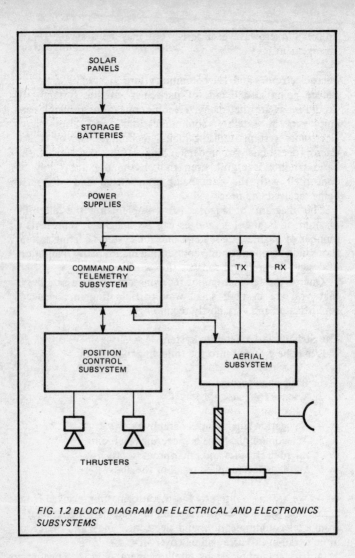

FIG. 1.2 BLOCK DIAGRAM OF ELECTRICAL AND ELECTRONICS SUBSYSTEMS

Although UoSATs for example, transmit at 10GHz in addition to VHF, they are not classed as communications satellites as they are non-commercial.

Having established some basic operating requirements and details we can now look in more detail at the facilities provided by one particular system, i.e. one for receiving UoSAT signals. Also, we can consider how such a receiver operates.

However, it is useful to also have at least some appreciation of the engineering aspects and also the scientific ones. Perhaps more importantly (or even essentially) a good understanding of some basic astronomical principles and navigation methods is required.

Before looking at the telecommunications (radio and microelectronics) systems in detail, we will look at the relevant considerations for points 1−4 inclusive, as listed previously, in the next chapter.

# Chapter 2

# APPLICATIONS

Apart from being complex and fascinating technological systems themselves satellites are placed and maintained in orbit for a specific reason. In other words they provide some sort of service, for example photographing the earth's surface, collecting scientific data or transmitting and receiving voice or data signals. Having said this, a satellite system comprises many sub-systems which are all essential when looking at its overall operation. These were listed in Chapter 1 and will now be described as follows.

## Engineering

In order to consider the operation of a satellite it is useful to select a specific one and investigate its operation in terms of its engineering function (i.e. how it maintains its orbit, derives its power and what its function is). In other words, the engineering hardware.

Artificial satellites comprise a sophisticated engineering system and a complex communications system and associated subsystems.

The engineering task involves designing and building the space vehicle which will operate in a very hostile environment (i.e. hard vacuum, temperature extremes, remoteness from the earth's surface and collision with space debris). The craft must also be able to withstand the forces applied in being lifted off by rocket or shuttle and be able to survive mechanically, electrically and electronically after leaving the earth's surface and atmosphere. It must obviously remain fully functional and be able to typically perform the following functions:

(i)  extend solar panels or sails;

(ii)  rotate in respect of its dish aerial (if fitted) and provide de-spin for same;

(iii)  follow an initial transfer orbit and then maintain a final

7

orbit (e.g. geostationary orbit) by operation of thrust motors as required.

By definition, an artificial satellite does not orbit the earth naturally but is the result of a combination of many complex engineering systems, the existence of which are far from obvious, but are outlined as follows.

A satellite is placed in orbit by the use of a powerful high speed rocket or ejected from a space vehicle such as 'Challenger'. The function of the rocket is to not only get the satellite to the required altitude (above the earth's atmosphere) but to also provide a suitable initial speed of orbit (orbital velocity) which is then maintained. This obviously requires much engineering and mathematical work, as the satellite is expected to orbit at a constant velocity and altitude until it reaches the end of its useful life.

In other words, the satellite must be able to maintain a specified orbit (altitude, position and velocity) and will require correction periodically. It follows then, that unless this could be achieved totally reliably and indefinitely, i.e. by autonomous control via on-board computers, then communication with a suitable earth station is required. This link can only be achieved by radio, and this is usually (but not always) done using microwave frequencies (3–30GHz).

We will return to the engineering aspects where relevant, but we will now look briefly at the relevant scientific aspects.

## Science

A satellite which orbits the earth at a given altitude and speed can be used to describe this phenomena as follows:

To maintain an orbit at 100km requires a velocity of 7.8km per second. This velocity ensures a state of equilibrium of the mass of the satellite in respect of the earth's gravitational force. If this speed reduces, the satellite will tend to descend and eventually pass through the atmosphere. If the speed increases, the altitude will increase and eventually the craft will leave the earth's orbit.

Without going into a great deal of detail about the engineering and mathematical considerations of placing the satellite in its particular orbit, it is useful to be aware that the orbit is of an ellipsular nature, rather than a circular one. This means

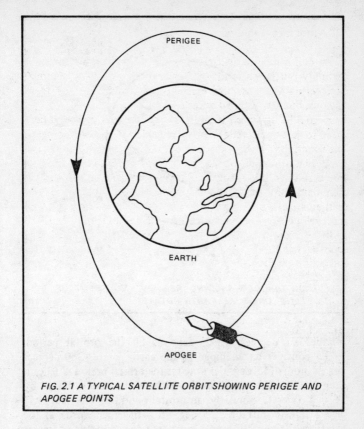

FIG. 2.1 A TYPICAL SATELLITE ORBIT SHOWING PERIGEE AND APOGEE POINTS

that it will have a maximum altitude above the earth and a minimum one, during each orbit. The lowest altitude is the perigee and the highest one the apogee. The reason for the non-circular orbit is that it is more difficult to maintain a constant speed in a circular orbit due to the variation of the earth's gravitational force, i.e. at the poles (see Figure 2.1).

An example of a satellite orbit is one which has an average height of 200km and an orbital period of 88mins. Another example could be 1500km altitude and 116mins.

Because the earth itself rotates, this means that a satellite's orbital plane (see Figure 2.2) effectively shifts to the left by a

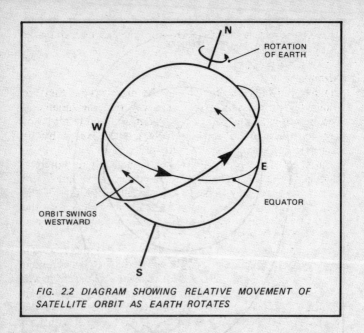

FIG. 2.2 DIAGRAM SHOWING RELATIVE MOVEMENT OF
SATELLITE ORBIT AS EARTH ROTATES

number of degrees which depends on the orbital period.

To consider an example, as the earth rotates 360 degrees per 24 hours (15 deg. per hour) if the orbital period is 1 hour, then the satellite transit path will have effectively shifted by 15 deg. (west). Similarly, an orbital period of 1.5 hours will give a transit shift of 22.5 deg. etc. In other words, as the rotation of the earth is anticlockwise (viewed looking down at the North Pole), although the actual satellite orbit does not change with respect to earth, the effect is as if it had moved westward (taking earth rotation as West–East).

Obviously these factors must be taken into account when predicting satellite passes (or just appreciating what is happening when referring to prediction information supplied).

A satellite orbit is described as a polar orbit if the craft passes over the North and South Poles say, every four hours. 'Sun synchronised' is another way of saying that the satellite has the same ground track each day and thus its appearance can be estimated or predicted easily. A geostationary satellite orbit is one where the satellite orbits at a very high altitude, e.g. 36,000km, at a speed in relation to the earth which makes it 'appear' to be stationary.

## Astronomy

Satellites can only be observed in the night sky, as they are illuminated by the sun in the same way that the moon and stars are, providing us with a good 'contrast' picture. It is not easy to distinguish a satellite from a star, except by its obvious steady movement across the sky.

Satellites can be confused with night-flying aircraft, although these are usually recognised by their noise and quite brightly flashing lights. A knowledge of some of the more well-known star formations (and points of the compass) will assist 'spotting' along with prediction information about the particular satellite to be observed.

The diagram in Figure 2.3 shows the limitations on satellite observations and it can be seen that the optimum (or only) viewing periods are after twilight and before dawn. It can also be seen that from position P a satellite at S with an altitude of 6000km is too far away to be observed and the altitude will increase as P is moved along the earth's surface in a clockwise direction. (Careful study of Figure 2.3 should make this clear.)

## Navigation

In addition to altitude information, longitude and latitude bearings are essential to locating the exact three-dimensional position of a satellite.

Very simply, longitude has a reference 'imaginary line' drawn from the North Pole to the South Pole which is marked as 0 degrees running through the Greenwich meridian. Atlases and maps are generally divided into 10 deg. segments going west from 0 deg. up to 180 deg. and also east up to 180 deg. Similarly, latitude is marked as a grid system at right angles to longitude with reference 0 deg. going in steps of 10 deg. from the Equator in a north or south direction.

Figure 2.4 shows a simplified map which might be used for plotting or drawing predicted satellite 'passes' from information received. An example of predicted information which

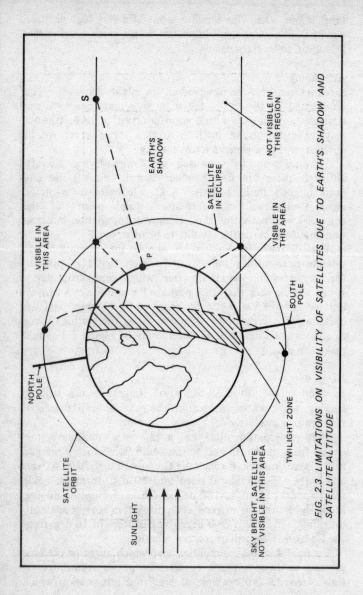

FIG. 2.3 LIMITATIONS ON VISIBILITY OF SATELLITES DUE TO EARTH'S SHADOW AND SATELLITE ALTITUDE

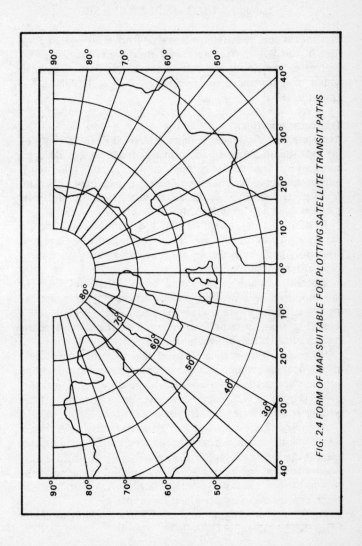

FIG. 2.4 FORM OF MAP SUITABLE FOR PLOTTING SATELLITE TRANSIT PATHS

13

may be supplied from a newspaper is:

London — 18.20—18.24 SW 64 S SE

This means that the satellite is visible from 6.20 — 6.24 p.m., rises in the South West, reaches a maximum elevation of 64 degrees in the South and sets in the South East. The map would of course need to be qualified with scale details, e.g. km/latitude.

## Telecommunications

Assuming that the reader is more interested in the activity of the satellite in terms of its 'primary' function, i.e. its communications facilities (e.g. television broadcast, telecomms, traffic, military, weather, spying, etc.), and how these are achieved technically, i.e. the electronics hardware (and software), we can now examine this.

In simple terms, an artificial satellite might be considered in the same way as a robot vehicle under the control of a microprocessor, but obviously we are now dealing in three dimensions instead of only two.

Whereas a robot vehicle could be modelled inexpensively and produced as a working micro-controlled system employing the usual hardware and software interfacing techniques, a satellite system is rather out of reach of the average micro enthusiast or college project lab!

However, when dealing with satellite systems a great deal of practical electronics, microelectronics and communications technologies can be used and demonstrated which can themselves provide a very comprehensive understanding of the systems and sub-systems employed.

Assuming that we are not in a position to pay or persuade NASA (North Atlantic Space Agency) or the ESA (European Space Agency) to launch a satellite craft (costing many thousands of pounds) complete with communications systems, we will instead concentrate on the satellites currently in orbit which provide radio signals which are of interest.

There are currently in excess of 2500 satellites in orbit, which can be categorised as follows:

| Communications (telecomms) | – | tv, telephone |
| Weather | – | earth surface pictures |
| Military | – | intelligence for all armed forces |
| Navigational | – | naval and commercial shipping |
| Spying (surveillance) | – | mainly US and USSR |

Before concentrating on one category, it is probably useful to pause and consider a fundamental operation of a satellite's activity.

## Telemetry, Tracking and Command

As previously mentioned many satellites transmit and receive radio signals at microwave frequencies which require expensive dish aerials. Other, lower frequencies are employed at UHF and also VHF frequencies. These may carry telemetry data relating to the status of the craft (e.g. functional tests, fuel availability, solar power, sensor information, etc.). Other signal information concerns tracking (position related to longitude and latitude on earth's surface), speed of craft, etc.

Control signals which effectively override computer controlled orbiting can also be effected at these lower frequencies.

Many satellites use these lower frequency (and inexpensive!) signal systems for the transmission and reception of main information (data), e.g. weather pictures.

Thus a microwave radio link is usually a vital part of any communications satellite system. As stated earlier however, this does not mean that all communication must be by microwave.

Microwave radio is suited to long distance (space) communication and uses minimum transmitting power as the radio signals consist of a very narrow and therefore highly directional beam.

It can be assumed then that control of the spacecraft is achieved by microwave signals, whereas information or traffic received by or transmitted from the satellite can be in the form of microwave, UHF or VHF signals. (Therefore microwave frequencies are not excluded for the carrying of actual traffic or data.)

Now that we have clarified this it will be clear that we can receive radio signals from a satellite with a suitable VHF or UHF receiver and a fairly simple (dipole) aerial.

Assuming for the moment that we have the equipment to receive transmitted signals from a chosen satellite, the next requirement is to decode the signals received. Although a radio receiver demodulates the RF carrier and produces an audio frequency output, the audio can actually consist of bursts or combinations of two frequencies. These correspond to logic levels 1 and 0. In other words, the demodulated audio provides digitally coded information.

This 'digital' information then requires decoding manually, or preferably using a suitable computer program. When this is achieved the computer can also be used to display the decoded information and provide a hard copy on a printer. The form of the data could be a table of results or readings from a scientific satellite or a weather map from one of the weather satellites.

We have now established the basic requirements for a home-based amateur satellite receiving station. Briefly, they are:

Suitable (dipole) aerial
Radio receiver (dedicated or wideband)
Decoder (hardware or software)
Microcomputer (with monitor and printer).

*Note:* The aerial will be wideband/omni-directional, so any 'tracking' will effectively be done manually!


**Some Suitable Systems**
Fortunately, from a home enthusiast's point of view, there are a number of non-commercial satellites in orbit which enable amateurs to make contact inexpensively and legally and are therefore suitable for home tracking.

Two systems of particular interest are the UoSAT series which provide telemetry data outputted from various transducers and scientific instruments on board, and the NOAA series which provide weather map data.

There are also a number of Soviet satellites, one specifically for use by amateurs (allowing transmitting and receiving) and also a weather satellite.

In later chapters we will take a closer look at the UoSAT series and the NOAA series.

## Basic System Details

The UoSAT satellite (also known as OSCAR) is the result of the work of the Department of Electronic and Electrical Engineering at the University of Surrey in Guildford (hence UoSAT). The alternative name OSCAR stands for Orbital Satellite Carrying Amateur Radio, indicating that one of the functions of the spacecraft is to allow amateur radio operators to transmit and receive signals to each other via space. The altitude of UoSAT is 554km, and its (polar) orbit is 95mins. Telemetry information is transmitted on 145.825MHz.

The block diagram in Figure 2.5 shows the equipment required to receive and decode signals from UoSAT.

The NOAA weather satellites transmit weather picture information. NOAA stands for the National Oceanic and Atmospheric Administration. They also have another name, i.e. TIROS, which describes their function — Television Infra Red Orbital Satellites.

The NOAA satellites all have a 101-minute polar orbits and transmit on 137.5MHz (NOAA-6 and NOAA-8) or 137.5 MHz (NOAA-7).

The diagram in Figure 2.5 also applies, but the receiver and decoder modules will be different.

Details of these two systems are only brief at this stage, but more detailed explanation will be covered in a later chapter.

Hopefully, this chapter will have succeeded in answering many questions about the concepts of satellite tracking and signal reception and will also have provided a clear overall picture of the mechanical engineering, scientific, astronomical, navigational and telecomms systems involved and their interaction.

I have not attempted to oversimplify the subject but tried to give an overall picture which will whet the appetite and encourage more people to take an interest. There are several very good books available on satellite communications which

17

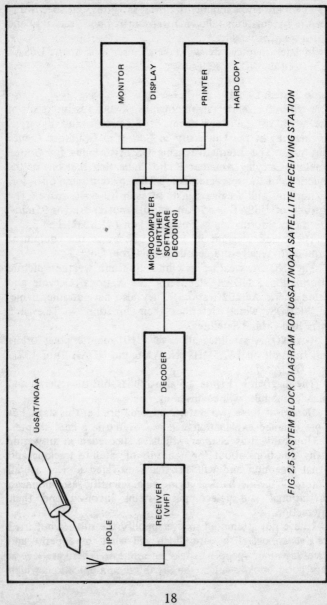

FIG. 2.5 SYSTEM BLOCK DIAGRAM FOR UoSAT/NOAA SATELLITE RECEIVING STATION

18

tend to be very detailed and mathematical and also very expensive. Details are included in Appendix 3 however, for further reading.

# Chapter 3

## AMSAT-UK

This organisation serves its members who are satellite enthusiasts, the majority of them being amateur radio operators and weather satellite listeners. AMSAT-UK is defined as the Radio Amateur satellite organisation of the United Kingdom and is affiliated to the Radio Society of Great Britain (RSGB). AMSAT-UK members pay an annual donation and receive a copy of OSCAR news every two months which is packed with informative and constructional articles on various aspects of receiving signals from both UoSAT (OSCAR) and NOAA satellites.

AMSAT-UK provides masses of technical information on UoSAT/OSCAR satellites, NOAA and Russian satellites (RS-5, -6, -7, -8) via its regular magazine and assorted leaflets and enclosures. It also provides up to date news of new craft and improvements to hardware including on-board computers and CCD cameras, speech synthesis, etc.

It is no exaggeration to describe the magazine as being a mine of information and details of other sources of information. Two particularly useful features are the Orbital Calendar supplied every two months and an order form detailing a comprehensive list of books, booklets and other satellite tracking aids, including software for the Amiga 500, Amstrad, Atari ST, BBC, Commodore 64, Spectrum 48K and IBM compatible PCs.

The Orbital Calendar contains dates and times of OSCAR 9, 10, 12, UoSAT-2 and other satellites. It is invaluable to those wishing to know exactly when a satellite is due overhead.

Information on Microsats (tiny satellites), PacSats (packet radio satellites) and also the new UoSAT-D craft are provided. Japanese satellites are also covered.

Much of the information and facilities provided are aimed at the 'expert' satellite enthusiast or experienced radio amateur but the beginner can benefit by weeding out essential information.

An example of the kind of useful information which can be

extracted from **AMSAT** publications is shown in the table of Figure 3.1.

| Satellite | Epoch Year | Frequency (MHz) |
|-----------|------------|-----------------|
| OSCAR 10  | 1988       | 145.810000      |
| OSCAR 11  | ..         | 145.825000      |
| OSCAR 12  | ..         | 435.795000      |
| OSCAR 13  | ..         | 145.812000      |
| RS 10/11  | ..         | 145.857000      |

FIG. 3.1    SATELLITE FREQUENCIES

A second example would be a detailed Glossary of Satellite Terms.

AMSAT-UK was formed in 1975, with the backing of AMSAT-USA. Members of the organisation have been engaged in the design and building of apparatus for OSCAR launches and associated user equipment and were directly involved in the building of the first UoSAT satellite.

AMSAT is a worldwide organisation with AMSAT-USA and BRAMSAT (AMSAT in Brazil) being particularly active and of interest to UoSAT users as will be seen in Chapter 4.

AMSAT-UK is the major source of up to the minute information for active satellite amateurs especially where accurate details of all current amateur satellites available are required. This organisation funded the original UoSAT Project and for example donated £27,000 to UoSAT in 1989.

**Objectives**
The objectives of **AMSAT-UK** are defined as follows by an extract from the constitution:

(a)    The promotion and development of space satellites for amateur radio communications and associated experimental, scientific or educational work;

(b)    Assisting in the above projects by suitable financial contributions at the discretion of the committee;

(c)    The propagation and dissemination of information pertaining to space satellite matters by instructive publication, lectures and radio transmissions in the Amateur Radio Frequency Bands.

Prospective members are asked to write to the Honorary Secretary enclosing a C5 SASE (see Appendix 1).

# Chapter 4

## UoSAT

In the first two chapters we looked at the overall satellite scene, concentrating on definitions, telecomms principles and also the engineering, scientific, astronomical and navigational implications.

Like the previous one, this chapter describes the activity of another very important organisation in the world of amateur satellite communications. It is the Department of Electrical and Electronic Engineering at the University of Surrey. The objective of the work carried out is to encourage educational interest and opportunity and also academic research.

### Scientific Usefulness

The following quotation from the University of Surrey Spacecraft Engineering Research Unit, Department of Electrical Engineering, effectively defines the mission objectives:

"1. Provides radio amateurs and professional scientists with a readily available tool to carry out studies of the near-earth electromagnetic environment and the relationship between solar and geomagnetic disturbances and their effect on radiowave propagation between hf and microwave frequencies.

2. To stimulate a greater degree of interest in space science in schools, colleges and universities by active participation, by ensuring that the experiments and housekeeping data are transmitted in such a manner that they are easily available, not only to professional scientists, but also to those users with very simple low-cost ground stations.

3. To broaden the scope of the Amateur Space Programme and to cater for the interests of the 'amateur scientist'.

4. To evaluate novel methods and new frequencies for use with later amateur spacecraft.

5.    To examine and demonstrate the feasibility of the design and construction of a relatively small and inexpensive spacecraft in this country, capable of a significant contribution to the scientific, engineering, amateur and educational communities."

## The UoSAT Series of Satellites

The UoSAT series were designed and built by the Department of Electronic and Electrical Engineering at the University of Surrey in Guildford. The alternative acronym OSCAR stands for Orbital Satellite Carrying Amateur Radio, indicating that one of the functions of the spacecraft is to allow amateur radio operators to transmit and receive signals to and from each other via space. The altitude of UoSAT-1 (or OSCAR 9) is 554km (344 miles) and its (polar) orbit is 95 minutes. Telemetry information is transmitted on 145.825MHz. The 'other' satellite is UoSAT-2 (or OSCAR 11). This orbits at 700km altitude with a (polar) orbit time of 98 minutes.

Both UoSATs transmit telemetry information relating to experimental data collected by on-board instruments, e.g. near-earth electromagnetic fields, solar and geomagnetic disturbances, etc. In addition to this, information concerning the spacecraft's on-board electronics, state of solar cells, etc. is provided.

Further detail can be found in the UoSAT Spacecraft Data Booklet (see Appendix 3). This consists of 40 A4 pages of very detailed descriptions of hardware, technical specifications, block diagrams of spacecraft, sub-units, etc.

The UoSAT satellites may not be considered to be as glamorous or as novel as the weather systems satellites, but it represents a realistic scientific application. Although these craft are hardly in the class of the recent Giotto vehicle investigating Halley's Comet in 1986, they can provide interesting and useful scientific data from space, for example, data on magnetic fields, temperature and regular readings concerning voltages and currents related to the on-board electronics and microelectronics.

The accident at Chernobyl in 1984 was also 'investigated' by UoSAT-1's radiation detector and although nothing conclusive was recorded, it could have been a case of 'no news is good news' — there is no incentive for hoping for a more interesting or tangible result! It is however, interesting to consider a scientific satellite's potential usefulness in this area. (A limitation of course, compared with an aeroplane is the much higher altitude of UoSATs, i.e. 500km for UoSAT-1, 700km for UoSAT-2. However, these altitudes are still more useful in this respect than the commercial geostationary orbits which operate at 36 000km.)

Having convinced ourselves of both the 'necessity' of building a satellite receiving station and of its technological and scientific merit, we can now think about what each type of system entails.

The intention of this chapter incidentally, is to encourage readers to set up a basic system and use it to learn about the subject, rather than spending too much time on unnecessary or excessive theory. Once established, the practical operation will provide the incentive to find out more about functional details.

## UoSAT-1
This satellite was launched on the 6th October 1981 at 11:27 GMT at the Western Space and Missile Centre, Vandenburg Air Force Base, California. The launch vehicle used was a Delta 2310 Rocket, but the UoSAT was a secondary 'payload' (as there was additional lift off power available on the rocket) to a somewhat more sophisticated spacecraft, the Solar Mesosphere Explorer Mission Spacecraft, launched by NASA. (At least UoSAT keeps good company!)

With an expected lifetime of one year, UoSAT-1 continued operating in low earth orbit for more than 8 years, and eventually burned up in the earth's atmosphere on 13th October 1989. In addition to many research experiments on the satellite, it carried a speech synthesiser under the control of the on-board computer, which 'spoke' telemetry and experiment data for direct reception.

UoSAT-1 maintained an altitude of 554km, and took 95 minutes for one (polar) orbit. Its speed can therefore be calculated using the earth's radius to find the length of one complete orbit. Taking this radius to be 6 370km, the distance covered is 43 505km (from $\pi \times d$) and therefore the

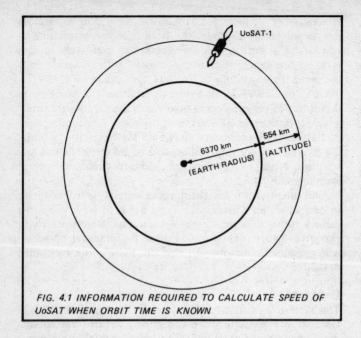

UoSAT-1

554 km
(ALTITUDE)

6370 km
(EARTH RADIUS)

*FIG. 4.1 INFORMATION REQUIRED TO CALCULATE SPEED OF UoSAT WHEN ORBIT TIME IS KNOWN*

speed can be calculated as approximately 7.6 km/sc (see Figure 4.1).

The complete calculation process is as follows:

circumference =

$$\pi \times d = \pi \times (6370 + 554)2$$
$$= 43\,504.77507$$
$$= 43\,505 \text{ km}$$

$$\text{time} = \frac{\text{distance (km)}}{\text{speed (km.s}^{-1})}$$

$$95 \text{ mins} = \frac{43\,505}{\text{speed}}$$

28

$$speed = \frac{43\ 505\ (km)}{95 \times 60\ (s)}$$

$$= 7.632$$

$$= \underline{8km.s^{-1}}$$

The calculation can be repeated for UoSAT-2 by substituting an altitude value of 700km which gives a circumference of 44,422km and a speed of $7.5km.s^{-1}$.

Work on this satellite was begun in January 1979 and its cost was around £100,000, mostly funded by British Industry, which also provided a great deal of technical assistance (AMSAT-UK donated £12,000). NASA launched the satellite free of charge.

The lifetime of this craft was about eight years, which puts its capital cost at something like £34 per day! The craft's lifetime can be defined as the time after which it is unable to maintain its speed and therefore its orbit. At this point it will re-enter the earth's atmosphere and burn up.

## UoSAT-2
This was launched on 1st March 1984 at 17:59 GMT at the same launch site as UoSAT-1. This time a Delta 3920 Rocket was used and the satellite was a secondary payload to the 1000kg LANDSAT-5 Earth resources satellite, again launched by NASA at only six months notice, when the earlier LANDSAT-4 failed prematurely.

UoSAT-2 orbits at 700km altitude with a polar orbit time of 98 minutes. As before the speed may be calculated from this information and is about 7.5km/sec.

This craft was completed in only five months. Its lifetime is longer, because of its higher altitude. At the time of publication of this book, UoSAT-2 is still operating well, now approaching 6 years in orbit and supporting a wide range of technology, engineering, communications and educational experiments.

## Technical Summary
Both UoSATs have provided facilities for measuring near-earth electromagnetic fields and also the relationships between solar

and geomagnetic disturbances. This is done in order to investigate the effects on radiowave propagation between hf and microwave frequencies.

Major systems on board UoSAT-1 provided telemetry information which was beamed to earth as digital modulation which can be decoded by a (home) computer. It is also equipped with a CCD (charge coupled device) slow-scan TV camera for taking pictures of the earth's surface. Unfortunately, this was not very successful, due to the spacecraft's spin.

UoSAT-2 is similar, but beams down more data in a form which can be readily decoded by the BBC Micro.

Both UoSATs transmitted telemetry information at 145.825MHz. Other frequencies are transmitted from 7.050 GHz to 10.47GHz. Obviously these require highly directional dish aerials. To receive telemetry at 145MHz requires a 2m narrow band FM receiver which must be able to cope with a Doppler Shift from 145.830MHz (approaching) to 145.810 MHz (receding).

UoSAT-1 transmitted "Digitalker" information (synthesised speech) on this frequency, plus a bulletin-board transmitted as ASCII text at 1200 baud. This binary information is encoded as 1200/2400Hz phase-synchronous AFSK. (This is similar to the BBC Micro's cassette interface format, except inverted in sense.)

UoSAT-2 transmits telemetry in the same way but its signals are directly compatible with the BBC Micro (no inversion required).

Figures 4.2 and 4.3 are block diagrams showing alternative systems of equipment needed to receive UoSAT signals.

Note that inversion is required for the data stream received from UoSAT-1.

This system is specifically for OSCAR-10 (non-UoSAT) using a (Wireless World design) hardware decoder, courtesy of G. J. Miller, AMSAT-UK.

An interesting comparison between these two systems is that the UoSAT decoding is carried out exclusively by software, whilst the OSCAR-10 system uses a hardware decoder and software for display purposes.

More details will be supplied later for specific products and complete systems available which can be bought/built to

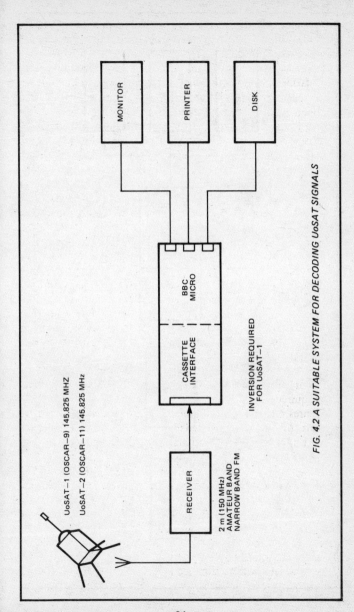

UoSAT—1 (OSCAR—9) 145.825 MHZ

UoSAT—2 (OSCAR—11) 145.825 MHz

MONITOR

PRINTER

DISK

BBC MICRO

CASSETTE INTERFACE

INVERSION REQUIRED FOR UoSAT—1

RECEIVER

2 m (150 MHz) AMATEUR BAND NARROW BAND FM

FIG. 4.2 A SUITABLE SYSTEM FOR DECODING UoSAT SIGNALS

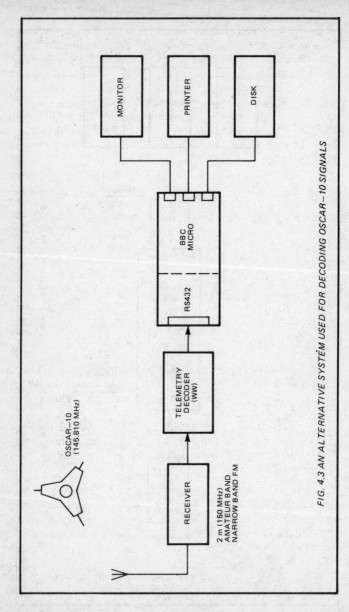

FIG. 4.3 AN ALTERNATIVE SYSTEM USED FOR DECODING OSCAR–10 SIGNALS

achieve reception, decoding and display. Details will also be included concerning the use of alternative microcomputers.

Although we have previously referred to the satellites we are particularly interested in (UoSAT 9, 11; OSCAR 10 and NOAA series) as communications satellites they are in fact strictly speaking in the amateur category.

A true communications satellite operates in the Gigahertz frequency range and carries maybe hundreds of traffic channels (e.g. telephone, data) which are operated on a commercial basis.

Although UoSATs, for example, transmit at 10GHz in addition to VHF, they are not classed as communications satellites as they are non-commercial.

Having established some basic operating requirements and details in the previous chapter, we can now look in more detail at the facilities provided by one particular system, i.e. one for receiving UoSAT signals. Also, we can consider how such a receiver operates.

### The Demise of UoSAT-1

Readers need not be alarmed to find that after eight years of successful operation, UoSAT-1 has decayed and is no longer transmitting (or existing!). UoSAT-2 is still operating on 145.825MHz but the 'alternative orbit' of UoSAT-1 is effectively replaced by the DOVE Microsatellite which was launched on 26th January 1990 into an 808km high circular sun-synchronous earth orbit, with an orbital period of 101 minutes.

Readers may be interested to note that UoSAT-1 continued to operate and transmit right up to the point of re-entering the earth's atmosphere and 'burning up' on Friday, 13th October 1989!

### The DOVE Satellite

DOVE (Digital Orbital Voice Encoder) is an educational project of the Brazilian amateur radio satellite organisation, BRAMSAT. This satellite transmits digitzed voice messages along with bulletins and spacecraft information spoken by its speech synthesiser (in English!).

DOVE appears above the horizon each day at around 10:30 a.m. and is in range for about 10 minutes. The satellite appears travelling in a southward direction around 10:30 a.m. and going northward at around 10:30 p.m., local time.

The DOVE satellite is intended to play an important role in the activities of the International Space Year in 1992. As its name implies, it is a 'cross-curricular/cross-cultural resource for the world's classroom, with an underlying theme of peace'.

DOVE is described as a polar orbiting platform which will transmit synthesised voice, digitized voice and short FSK packet radio streams. The basic content of DOVE's transmission will consist of the following:

ID: including time and sub-satellite point.

Bulletins: news, orbital elements and special projects.

Telemetry: selected and collected values from points on the spacecraft which allow monitoring of its condition in orbit.

The three major purposes of DOVE are:

1. A test bed for advanced space communications operations in the amateur radio bands.

2. An orbital tool to aid in the development of cross-curricular, cross-cultural activities/understanding in schools globally for students of all ages.

3. A stimulus for young people worldwide to become involved in amateur radio and technical careers.

DOVE is a nine inch cube, packed with computer and radio gear, thus the name Microsat. It is a digital satellite, that is, its transmissions are created and controlled by its on-board computer. Orbital calendar information is available via AMSAT-UK.

# Chapter 5

## NOAA

NOAA stands for "National Oceanic and Atmospheric Administration" which is the name of the American organisation which controls these satellites. The actual name of this series is TIROS (Television Infra-Red Orbital Satellites).

There are currently four satellites available, NOAA-6, -7, -8 and -9.

Each of these spacecraft have 101-minute sun-synchronous polar orbits, spread around the globe such that they do not interfere with each other.

NOAA-6, -8 and -9 transmit at 137.5MHz, whilst NOAA-7 transmits at 137.62MHz.

Due to the rotation of the earth, a satellite travelling in a roughly north—south orbit (polar) orbit will cross the Equator 25 degrees further west on each orbit. (The earth's spin is anti-clockwise looking down at the North Pole.) This enables the whole of the earth's surface to be covered. A satellite of this type will only pass within usable range two or three times every 12 hours.

To receive weather pictures from these satellites a wide-band AM receiver is required tuned to 137.5 or 137.62MHz.

A suitable system requirement is shown in Figure 5.1 and shows the equipment needed to track NOAA satellites. More detail concerning practical systems are covered in Chapter 8. A NOAA receiving system is of course limited to weather information, but has the potential for spectacular results on screen and of course printer. There is also tremendous scope for using or developing sophisticated tracking and display software.

### Automatic Picture Transmission

Each NOAA transmits weather pictures in the APT (Automatic Picture Transmission) format. This format produces one visible and one infra-red image side-by-side, transmitted at 120 lines per minute.

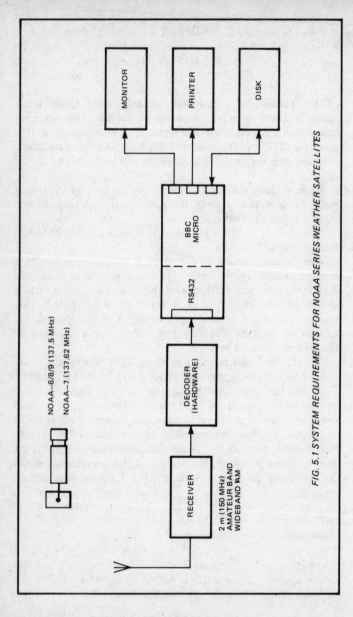

FIG. 5.1 SYSTEM REQUIREMENTS FOR NOAA SERIES WEATHER SATELLITES

The lines of picture information build up a picture in a slow raster form, but the picture is a continuous strip following the path of the satellite over the ground.

A more technical description of the APT format, used by most weather satellites is described as follows.

The radio frequency carrier is modulated by a 2.4KHz sub-carrier whose amplitude is modulated by the picture information and synchronising signals.

Figure 5.2 shows the subcarrier envelope for a typical line of APT information, including sync pulses.

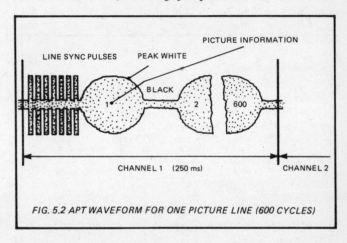

FIG. 5.2 APT WAVEFORM FOR ONE PICTURE LINE (600 CYCLES)

The waveform diagram represents a single picture line transmitted as a one-quarter of a second burst of modulated subcarrier. This is actually an audible (2400Hz) tone. Each line is 600 cycles of subcarrier. (A full envelope diagram would need to show 600 individual 'blobs' of picture information to represent one picture line on the screen.)

The complete signal for one line occupies 250ms, derived from:

$$\frac{600 \text{ cycles}}{2400 \text{ cycles.sec}} = 0.25 \text{ sec}$$

It follows then, that the carrier (2.4KHz) contains modulation

37

information for 2400/600 = 4 picture lines.

It can be seen from the diagram that the peak white picture level corresponds to maximum subcarrier level and black to minimum.

The APT signal provides visible picture information alternately with infra-red. Thus the signal is made up of Channel 1 – visible (for 600Hz of subcarrier, or 250ms) and Channel 2 – infra-red for the same length of time. In other words, the picture information sequence is Channel 1, 2, 1, 2, etc. or visible, infra-red, visible, infra-red, etc. (This sequence occurs once every second and is illustrated simply in Figure 5.3.)

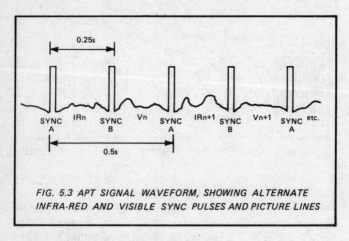

FIG. 5.3 APT SIGNAL WAVEFORM, SHOWING ALTERNATE INFRA-RED AND VISIBLE SYNC PULSES AND PICTURE LINES

The maximum horizontal definition is 600 pixels, where each pixel position corresponds to one of the 600 'blobs' in each APT picture line waveform.

Channel 1 (visible) provides 7 sync pulses at 1040 pulses per second, whilst Channel 2 (infra-red) provides 7 sync pulses at 832 pulses per second.

# Chapter 6

# METEOSAT

Meteosat is the European part of a chain of five geostationary weather satellites which ring the earth. Meteosat 1 was launched in November 1977 by the European Space Agency and was active until November 1979. In June 1981 Meteosat 2 was launched to replace this. To be geostationary Meteosat has to have an altitude of 36,000 kilometres in an 'orbit' around the Equator. The speed of the satellite (in relation to the earth) ensures that it is effectively stationary over the Greenwich Meridian (0 degrees N, 0 degrees E). In other words the satellite orbits on the same axis as the earth at a speed which maintains it in a fixed position above the earth (geostationary). From that location it can scan between a third and a half of the earth's surface, including Europe, continuously transmitting pictures 24 hours a day. Figure 6.1 shows the actual global coverage possible using a chain of geostationary satellites.

Because the satellite is so far away, a dish aerial is required to receive picture signals. Unlike the polar orbiters, Meteosat does not transmit direct to your ground station. The infra-red and visible scanning data is first beamed down to the control station in West Germany where it is processed (computer enhanced) and sent back up to Meteosat for broadcast. The pictures are then transmitted in segments according to a fixed daily schedule, arriving at your receiver a few minutes after they were taken. Meteosat also relays pictures from other geostationary satellites in the chain.

**Earth Views**
Meteosat looks at the whole of the earth (between one-third to one-half of its surface) at once. It looks through a device called a multispectral radiometer which provides four separate images, two visible and two in different infra-red bands. One infra-red channel gives a thermal image of the earth, the other image is based on a water vapour absorption band indicating levels of atmospheric humidity.

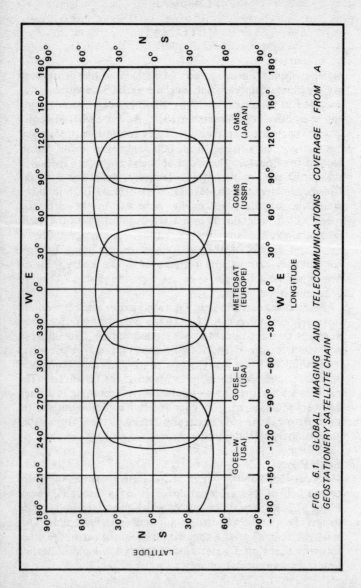

FIG. 6.1 GLOBAL IMAGING AND TELECOMMUNICATIONS COVERAGE FROM A GEOSTATIONERY SATELLITE CHAIN

40

Raw data is transmitted to the earth for processing in the S frequency band (1670–2110MHz). These signals are received at the Data Acquisition, Telemetry and Tracking Station (DATTS) in Michelstadt about 50 kilometres from Darmstadt in East Germany.

These signals are then fed by landline to the Meteosat Ground Computer system at the European Space Operations Centre in Darmstadt.

The data is then processed by a pair of mainframe computers from which information is fed by landline to worldwide users and also back to DATTS for re-transmission to the satellite in WEFAX format, with coastline added (superimposed).

This processed data is re-radiated by the satellite on two S band frequencies, Channel A at 1694.5MHz and Channel B at 1691MHz (Down Converter).

Figure 6.2 is a simple diagram of the Meteosat 2 and Ground Station.

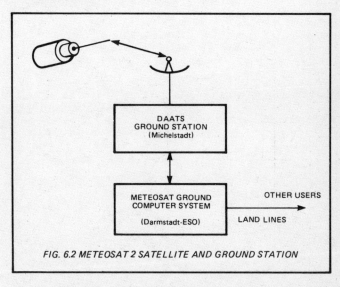

FIG. 6.2 METEOSAT 2 SATELLITE AND GROUND STATION

Pictures are transmitted by the WEFAX system, which is similar to the APT system of NOAA, but of a much higher quality. These signals are transmitted at 1.6945GHz (linearly polarised). A dish aerial of at least one metre diameter is required with a 1694.5MHz to 137MHz frequency converter mounted as close to the pick-up as possible. This aerial/converter system can then be connected to a 137MHz NOAA weather receiver. Although dish aerials are highly directional they can be fixed in position as the satellite appears to be stationary in the sky.

The Meteosat 2 picture signals, like the NOAA APT signals have 7 sync pulses at a rate of 840 pulses per second, but in addition there are 300 sync pulses per second and 450 per second for start and stop frame synchronisation respectively.

# Chapter 7

# A UoSAT GROUND STATION

We can now look at one or two practical systems which enable UoSAT signals to be received, decoded and processed using currently available systems. Although suppliers may suddenly or eventually change or cease a particular product the ones we look at will be helpful in demonstrating the principles involved and will leave the reader with an understanding of how to approach the problem of getting data from an amateur satellite.

One (complete) system available for use with a home computer such as the BBC Micro (and also the ageing Electron, Spectrum and Spectrum Plus) is the ASTRID, which was produced by SRL Communications in Yorkshire. Unfortunately this is no longer manufactured but its operation is worth describing, as one typical system that I have had 'hands on' experience with and also examples may still be available on the second-hand market as it was a particularly popular and low priced receiver.

The ASTRID is a radio receiver and hardware decoder contained in a single steel case. It also includes an audio stage complete with speaker. A power supply with built-in plug and also a dipole aerial and cable are included. The system is complete, apart from a suitable home computer with serial port (RS232, RS423) and an ordinary cassette recorder.

Figure 7.1 is a block diagram showing connections to ASTRID (refer also to Figure 2.5 diagram in Chapter 2).

## Information Content

Information transmitted by UoSAT scientific satellites contains telemetry data and news builletins. The telemetry data itself contains details of experiments or measurements being made by on-board sensors and also information about electronics circuits and battery voltages. The news bulletins contain information which is regularly transmitted from the ground station at University of Surrey. This news concerns such things as weather satellite information, orbital parameters

43

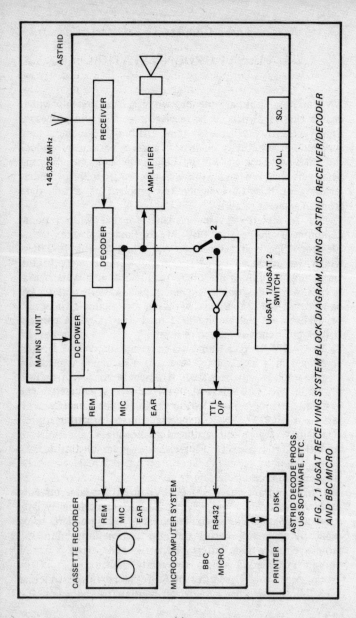

FIG. 7.1 UoSAT RECEIVING SYSTEM BLOCK DIAGRAM, USING ASTRID RECEIVER/DECODER AND BBC MICRO

of UoSATs, OSCARs, NOAA and general satellite and space news (e.g. space shuttle reports).

"Digitalker" speech information is also transmitted which is decoded as spoken numbers in the ASTRID speaker. These are then decoded manually using a look-up table or software.

There are a total of 60 telemetry readings and 45 experimental status points.

## Operating ASTRID (Technical Description)

A UoSAT satellite transmits its telemetry and news information which is frequency modulated on to a 145.825MHz carrier. The modulation is 1200 baud.

This is decoded internally and audio tones of 1200Hz (logic 0) and 2400Hz (logic 1) are fed into the cassette port. This is in the form of asynchronous data.

The system has been designed to operate without connection to a computer, i.e. it can capture data by a received radio signal opening the squelch on the ASTRID receiver and also switching on the cassette recorder via its REMote socket. On the BBC Micro, this is exactly the same system used by the cassette interface port. This means that the ASTRID can be left unattended (drawing 100mA at 16 volts on standby) and of course no power being drawn (from batteries) until the cassette is REMotely switched.

Following a satellite 'pass' and successful reception and decoding, the results which should be stored on cassette can be loaded into the micro say, next morning and examined on screen or printer. (For convenience, this information can be retained on cassette or transferred to disk.)

The ASTRID package is supplied with a demonstration data tape, containing typical data information which would be received following a satellite pass. A program is also included which 'decodes' the data. However this only provides the raw data formatted on the screen. This data can be manually decoded referring to the coding method in the ASTRID handbook. This is fairly tedious and better done with software. Suitable software is available from AMSAT-UK in the form of two disks called SATPACK (see Appendix 1).

The first disk provides a map of the earth with satellite orbits shown with respect to time and is of real practical use in establishing when the satellite will next appear over the horizon.

A second disk decodes fully the telemetry data received from a UoSAT and displays it on the screen or printer.

Providing that the aerial is appropriately sited, an adequate signal and sufficient data can be received from a pass, and therefore tracking of the satellite is not necessary. This is because of the (VHF) frequencies being used and also the relatively low altitude (500km) compared to communications satellites operating at 36,000km (22,370 miles)!

A typical aerial would be a 1 metre dipole, being omni-directional and therefore relatively low gain. Higher gain can be achieved by the addition of a reflector, but making the aerial more directional and therefore approaching a tracking requirement!

At this point it is worth mentioning that the orbit time of a UoSAT is approximately 90 minutes, with an effective shift of 24 degrees of its orbital path, due to the rotation of the earth. A simple calculation, 360 (degrees) divided by 24 (hours) represents 15 different polar orbits of the earth every 24 hours. Also, it is useful to know that the maximum pass time is no more than ten minutes.


### Specification

The ASTRID unit contains a superheterodyne receiver operating at 145.825MHz. Its bandwidth is 12KHz and its sensitivity 0.2$\mu$V. Audio output is 0.3W into its 8 ohm speaker. Aerial impedance is 75 ohms. As already stated, dc consumption on standby is 100mA at 16 volts.

The output level to tape is 50mV p-to-p and the decoder input level 200mV p-to-p. A TTL output is also provided, if required for external logic circuits, such as the RS232 input to a computer.

Data transmitted from UoSAT is in the same form as that required by the BBC Micro cassette interface, i.e. asynchronous data (AFSK) with tones of 1200Hz (logic 0) and 2400Hz (logic 1). The baud rate is 1200, utilising TTL signals as ASCII text. The format is 1 start, 7 data, 1 even parity and 2 stop bits (11 total).

## Software

Although the ASTRID package includes a cassette with a sample quantity of data and simple decoding programs for UoSAT 1 and 2, additional software is available to decode and display the information.

Unless a user wishes to write his or her own decoding programs, software such as SATPACK can be obtained, as already mentioned. This consists of two disks. The first one displays satellite orbit information in tabular or map form and also sends data to the RS423 port to enable the real time control of a tracking aerial, if required.

The second disk contains a suite of sophisticated data handling programs, specifically written to decode the telemetry from UoSAT 2. This data is 'processed', i.e. translated into numerical data which is analysed for errors and can then be stored on disk as a 'processed data file'.

Other UoSAT software is available from AMSAT-UK.

Software is also available for the Spectrum 48K and Spectrum Plus.

## Other Micros

Although hardware connection to the system is very easy and straightforward in the case of the BBC Micro, it is also possible to easily connect the ASTRID decoder output to the Electron (with official serial port) and to the Sinclair Spectrum (with Sinclair Interface 1 unit).

The experienced micro enthusiast should not find it difficult to interface to his or her machine as the data format is straightforward (serial) TTL ASCII.

## Interference

Most micros generate RF interference, so problems may be encountered when using the standard (low gain) dipole, especially at low 'altitude' − like ten feet! For this reason, ASTRID is designed to be easily operated 'off-line' and data captured without the micro being used (or even switched on).

If the unit is operated in a low electrical interference area, it is possible to receive data 'live' from an overhead pass, but then the data can not be stored on cassette or disk. Also, problems may arise due to RF interference generated by the computer itself.

Interference needs to be considered, but should not prevent reception, even if it depends on 'auto' reception during the night.

## Conclusions

We have now looked at an example of one commercial available complete system, the ASTRID, for UoSAT satellites. This should have provided an insight into what is required in terms of hardware (radio and computer) and software (for decoding and display). Hopefully, the aspiring satellite enthusiast will appreciate that dealing with satellites is not necessarily complex, but requires a certain ability to see it as a system rather than a simple self-contained unit.

## A Unilab System

Another complete receiving and decoding system example is provided by Unilab. This system is intended for use with the BBC Micro B, B+ or Master 128 micros. A monitor (colour if possible), printer (Epson FX80 type preferably), disk drive and cassette recorder are required.

## Unilab System Outline

The UoSAT Ground Station package is detailed as follows:

UoSAT Receiver, with leads
UoSAT Data Demodulator, with lead
UoSAT Receiver Antenna, with phasing harness
UoSAT RF pre-amplifier
Coaxial cable, 10 metres with connectors
SAT-PACK 1 Orbital Prediction software (40T disk, manual)
SAT-PACK 2 and 3 Telemetry and Graphics software (3 X 40T discs, sample tape, manual)
Surrey University Data Display software (2 X 40T discs, manual)
Surrey University Data Display Booklet
Schools Satellite Project Master Manual

Apart from the BBC Micro system (detailed later), everything required for a fully operational ground station is provided.

Figure 7.2 shows the basic set-up for the complete receiving, decoding and displaying system.

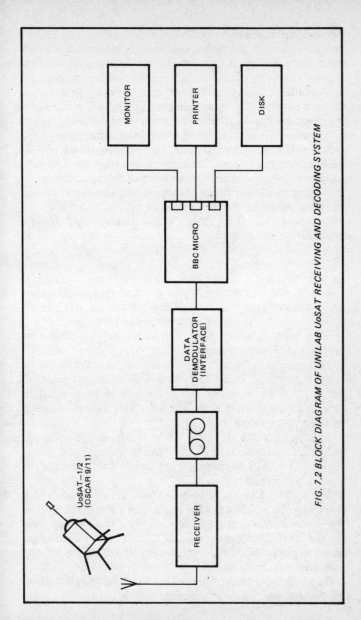

FIG. 7.2 BLOCK DIAGRAM OF UNILAB UoSAT RECEIVING AND DECODING SYSTEM

## Ground Station Package

Before looking at the system components in detail it is worth mentioning that the documentation and full range of software is quite substantial and consists of three packages with a total of six disks, 1 cassette and 3 software manuals. In addition, there is the Master Manual (detailing UoSAT and NOAA systems) and the University of Surrey booklet which is very informative. Compared to the Unilab Weather System the software is more substantial, as it plays a very large part in dealing with the received data. In some ways the raw data received is of very little value without all of the software. It is possible to decode data manually or even to write your own decoding programs, but this would be rather tedious and very time consuming. The software and its facilities represents a major part of the system.

## Aerial

The aerial is a 5-element left-hand circularly polarised crossed Yagi, consisting of one pair of crossed dipoles, one pair of crossed reflectors and three pairs of crossed deflectors.

This aerial is rather large and would require substantial support, particularly if roof mounted.

Although it is highly directional due to the number of director elements, it can be used usefully in a fixed position. An optional RF amplifier can be used to improve signal to noise ratio and provide error-free text. This is simply inserted between the aerial and coax feeder.

Full instructions are given on assembly and installation, including the connection of the phasing harness. All that is required is a small screwdriver and an adjustable spanner for mounting the aerial on to a mast.

My test installation consisted of the aerial clamped to a broom handle which was then gripped in a Black and Decker Workmate in the centre of the lawn (this method was used for the weather receiver aerial, see Chapter 8). This arrangement worked OK, but was pushing the strength of the (wooden) mast to its limits!

Ten metres of coax cable terminated by BNC plug at the receiver end and N-type at the aerial end are provided.

**Receiver**

The receiver unit is in the form of a flat orange topped steel case measuring about 24cm X 13cm X 4cm. It is clearly labelled for connection of aerial (BNC socket), power supply (banana sockets) and a 75 ohm type 'aerial' socket for connection to tape recorder (MIC) input. A 4mm jack socket enables connection to the REMote socket of a portable cassette recorder. Aerial and cassette leads are included. As the unit is intended for school lab use a bench power supply is assumed to be easily available. Another reason for this is that the 16–18V a.c. or d.c. supply input can be achieved using lamp batteries, enabling the receiver to be operated outside, without the constraints of mains supplies. Presumably an optional mains unit would increase the cost of the unit and also make it slightly heavier. Current requirements are typically 150mA.

The receiver unit includes an audio amplifier and speaker which enables the monitoring of the satellite signal during (attended) recordings (or just listening to a pass). This audio output is also 'tapped off' and outputted to the tape recorder.

In addition to the volume control a squelch control can be used to adjust the signal level which will activate the receiver and also turn on the recorder.

A Doppler monitor output is provided for those interested in observing carrier frequency changes as the satellite progresses towards and past the ground station.

After connecting up the receiver to the aerial and tape recorder, the squelch is set to just turn off the recorder remotely. The unit is then left to record the next pass or passes, after remembering to depress the record keys and also switching on the external power supply!

Unless in attendance, or having information available about pass times (more on this later), the unit can be left on overnight, or more usefully, during the day.

Before embarking on the recording and then processing of received signals, it is good strategy to familiarise yourself with the system using the program disk (SAT-PACK 2/3) and sample tape.

This is clearly explained in the Master Manual and also the software booklet accompanying the disk.

*Note:* Receiving satellite signals does not require the operation of the computer system, unless it is required to receive and monitor live passes. However, this is not very practical. due to the RF interference generated by the computer itself.

I will return to the use of software and the processing of received data after looking at the next part of the hardware, namely the Data Demodulator (interface) unit.

### Data Demodulator (Interface)

The data demodulator unit is another flat box which matches the receiver in size and appearance. It has a mains psu, coax input from cassette (EAR) output and a switch to select UoSAT-1 (OSCAR 9) or UoSAT-2 (OSCAR 11). Output from the demodulator is via multi-way cable to BBC RS423 input.

### Operating the System

The Unilab Master Manual provides full instructions on how to drive the system including details of using software and menu, but more detail is included in the individual software manuals.

Very simply, the receiver automatically outputs audio tones on to cassette tape. Once recorded, these tones need to be loaded into the BBC Micro via the interface unit (Data Demodulator).

Raw data from tape can be examined as follows:

Either using:
　　UoSAT Data Display disc 2 (option 3, 1200 baud).
　　This provides screen display only.

Or using:
　　SAT-PACK 2 (option 4).
　　This creates raw data files which can then be printed.

At this stage, use of the 'INPUT POLARITY' and 'SIGNAL INVERT' switches can be made and a meaningful data stream produced. This crude 'guessing' method is necessary, unless you have definite information on particular passes, i.e. which satellite and whether data is inverted or not.

General familiarty will also enable the user to deal with several passes situated 'serially' on the same cassette tape, including noisy sections around auto switch on and switch off.

The limitations of the raw data received and displayed will soon be realised, although it is useful and of educational value to be able to see the 'unformatted' telemetry as it arrives at the aerial.

## Data Display Software

The significance of the data processing software can now be demonstrated by using the UoSAT Data Display software for both UoSAT-1 and UoSAT-2. This produces whole orbit data (WOD), including graphs of chosen parameters. Also, real-time telemetry data is displayed, for the monitoring of analogue measurements and digital status points.

SAT-PACK 2 and 3 for UoSAT-2 produces data in the form of graphs and tables.

## Some Sample Results

Figure 7.3 is an extract from the orbital prediction calendar which is supplied to members of AMSAT-UK. In this example data is for OSCAR-9 (UoSAT-1), although this craft is now defunct.

Figure 7.4 is an example of the menus encountered when using SAT-PACK disk 2.

Figure 7.5 shows raw data for UoSAT-2.

Figure 7.6 is an example of part of a printout of raw telemetry data which has been processed into tabular form.

Figure 7.7 is a full telemetry printout (60 channels).

Figure 7.8 is an alternative numeric data display.

## Technical Details

LEQX is the latitude position at which the UoSAT craft crosses the 0 degree longitude Equator in an approximately S–N direction.

Satellite crossings are usually stated as being between 0–360 deg. W, although maps use 0–180 deg. W (clockwise) and 0–180 deg. E (anti-clockwise).

Pass time (horizon to horizon) is 10–15 minutes, with usually no more than 10 minutes of 'useful' data.

FIG. 7.3 ORBITAL PREDICTION CALENDAR EXTRACT
(reproduced by permission of AMSAT-UK)

```
    AMSAT-UK CALENDAR.        AMSAT OSCAR-9          MAY - JUNE   1987

        This Calendar gives the predicted EQX for only those Orbits.
    that will at sometime during the pass be in range of somewhere in the UK.


OSCAR9  08-05-87    OSCAR9  09-05-87    OSCAR9  10-05-87    OSCAR9  11-05-87
04:25:26   147 >    03:58:31   141 >    05:06:00   157 >    04:39:11   151 >
05:59:39   171 >    05:32:50   164 >    06:40:13   181 <    06:13:23   174 >
07:33:52   194 <    07:07:02   188 <    08:14:26   205 <    07:47:36   198 <
09:08:05   218 <    08:41:15   211 <    09:48:38   228 <    09:21:49   221 <
15:24:55   312 <    10:15:28   235 <    16:05:29   322 <    15:38:39   316 <
16:59:08   336 <    14:58:06   305 <    17:39:42   346 <    17:12:52   339 <
18:33:21   359 <    16:32:19   329 <    19:13:54     9 >    18:47:05     3 >
20:07:34    23 >    18:06:31   353 <                        20:21:17    26 >
                    19:40:44    16 >

OSCAR9  12-05-87    OSCAR9  13-05-87    OSCAR9  14-05-87    OSCAR9  15-05-87
04:12:21   144 >    05:19:43   161 >    04:52:53   154 >    04:26:03   147 >
05:46:33   167 >    06:53:56   184 <    06:27:06   178 >    06:00:15   171 >
07:20:46   191 <    08:28:09   208 <    08:01:18   201 <    07:34:28   194 <
08:54:59   215 <    10:02:21   231 <    09:35:31   225 <    09:08:41   218 <
15:11:49   309 <    16:19:12   326 <    15:52:22   319 <    15:25:31   312 <
16:46:02   332 <    17:53:25   349 <    17:26:34   342 <    16:59:44   336 <
18:20:15   356 <    19:27:37    13 >    19:00:47     6 >    18:33:57   359 <
19:54:27    19 >                        20:35:00    29 >    20:08:09    23 >

OSCAR9  16-05-87    OSCAR9  17-05-87    OSCAR9  18-05-87    OSCAR9  19-05-87
03:59:12   140 >    05:06:34   157 >    04:39:44   150 >    04:12:53   144 >
05:33:25   164 >    06:40:47   181 <    06:13:56   174 >    05:47:05   167 >
07:07:38   188 <    08:15:00   204 <    07:48:09   198 <    07:21:18   191 <
08:41:50   211 <    09:49:12   228 <    09:22:21   221 <    08:55:30   214 <
10:16:03   235 <    16:06:03   322 <    15:39:12   315 <    15:12:21   309 <
14:58:41   305 <    17:40:15   346 <    17:13:24   339 <    16:46:33   332 <
16:32:53   329 <    19:14:28     9 >    18:47:37     2 >    18:20:46   356 <
18:07:06   352 <                        20:21:50    26 >    19:54:59    19 >
19:41:19    16 >
```

Altitude:                    UoSAT-1 — 554km
                             UoSAT-2 — 700km

Orbit time:                  UoSAT-1 — 95 minutes
                             UoSAT-2 — 98 minutes

RF carrier frequency:        UoSAT-1 — 145.825MHz
                             UoSAT-2 — 145.825MHz


## Conclusions

The Unilab system is very easy to use, being well organised and
fully documented. I found that the system worked first time,
with no problems, apart from basic familiarsation.

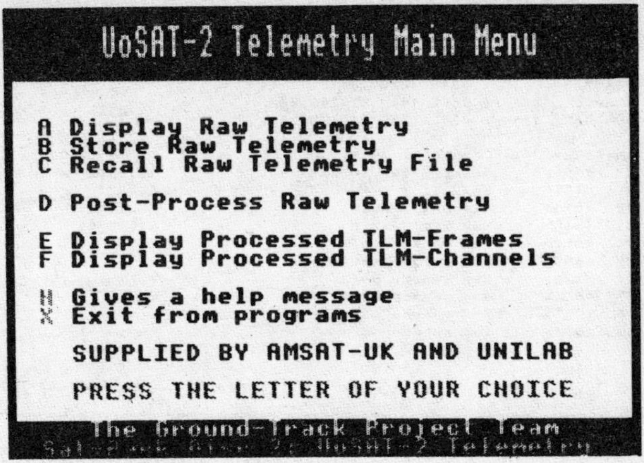

```
        UoSAT-2 Telemetry Main Menu


    A Display Raw Telemetry
    B Store Raw Telemetry
    C Recall Raw Telemetry File

    D Post-Process Raw Telemetry

    E Display Processed TLM-Frames
    F Display Processed TLM-Channels

    H Gives a help message
    X Exit from programs

    SUPPLIED BY AMSAT-UK AND UNILAB

    PRESS THE LETTER OF YOUR CHOICE

    The Ground-Track Project Team
    Sat-Pack  Area 2: UoSAT-2 Telemetry
```

FIG. 7.4    SAT–PACK SCREEN MENU (AMSAT–UK AND UNILAB)

```
**************************************************
   Sat-Pack:  UoSAT-2 RAW TELEMETRY FILE DISPLAY
   Reading from file: R.TEST-2
**************************************************
:UOSAT-2              8510270104147
00503601499502671203352704052305039F06025107052008047B09037I
103064113322120003130640141128E15440416181F175120184739195386
20378E21184E22660023000124000625000726097A27557228515B295248
30512531040632286D33577534000735268A36320437430338476E39504B
407672411206426426430667441670450001460002474944485067494768
50579E51102752680953686E54658A550000560003575007584944595507E
60826A615BE7621F4E633305644402651705665866B67700668000E69000F
:UOSAT-2              8510270104133
00505001478A02673003349D04052305039F06025107052008047B09037D
10295F1133221200031306371412296F15440416181F175157184863195397
20443121184E22660023000124000625000726097A27556328512C295248
30513431040632286D33579B34000735265736317037430338476E39504B
407663411206426426430632441661450001460002474944485067494779
50563551102752676053682A5465315500005600035749965845944595507E
60826A615BE7621F4E633305644402651705665647ED67700668000E69000F
```

FIG. 7.5    RAW DATA DISPLAY (AMSAT–UK AND UNILAB)

```
UoSAT-2 SATELLITE TELEMETRY

Source file: 'P.TEST-1'

FRAME No.      : 8510270104128      (1)
Mission time  : 27/10/85   10:41:28
AOS date/time : 27/10/85   10:39 hrs.

Analogue Data Channels: 00-59
00  <506>      Solar array current -Y      19.0000      mA.
01  <468>      Nav mag X axis              1.4980       uT.
02  <673>      Nav mag Z axis              33.1979      uT.
03  <348>      Nav mag Y axis              -16.5564     uT.
04  <052>      Sun sensor no.1             <      >
05  <039>      Sun sensor no.2             <      >
06  <025>      Sun sensor no.3             <      >
07  <052>      Sun sensor no.4             <      >
08  <047>      Sun sensor no.5             <      >
09  <037>      Sun sensor no.6             <      >
```

FIG. 7.6
PROCESSED TELEMETRY DATA SAMPLE (AMSAT–UK AND UNILAB)

This system provides a fairly cheap and reliable means of capturing data from the UoSAT craft currently in orbit. It is fully supported by some fairly comprehensive and sophisticated software.

Anyone who is interested in satellite activities and also scientific measurements made in space can have access to a reasonably sophisticated satellite system in terms of hardware (space, computer and radio) and a suite of software which enables some very detailed data processing and display. The Unilab system enables the bringing together of physics, space engineering, digital and analogue electronics including microprocessor systems and telecommunications. It also provides an insight into the operation of commercial communications satellites.

### Cirkit UoSAT / 2m Receiver

This is a six-channel receiver (2 VHF and 4 × 2m amateur band) with 144–164MHz bandwidth .

Further details, technical specification, etc. is available from the current Cirkit catalogue (see Appendix 2).

This receiver is a pcb kit and requires additional hardware interfacing for computer operation and accompanying software.

Figure 7.9 shows how basic the 'system' is!

```
Source file: 'P.UOSAT11'

FRAME No.      : 8705310194127      (6)
Mission time   : 31/05/87   19:41:27
AOS date/time  : 01/06/87   00:00 hrs.

Analogue Data Channels: 00-59
00  <100>  Solar array current -Y        790.4000    mA.
01  <070>  Nav mag X axis                -57.6050    uT.
02  <742>  Nav mag Z axis                43.7066     uT.
03  <000>  Nav mag Y axis                -69.0000    uT.
04  <000>  Sun sensor no.1               <       >
05  <338>  Sun sensor no.2               <       >
06  <211>  Sun sensor no.3               <       >
07  <461>  Sun sensor no.4               <       >
08  <474>  Sun sensor no.5               <       >
09  <322>  Sun sensor no.6               <       >
10  <140>  Solar array current +Y        714.4000    mA.
11  <250>  Nav mag (wing) temp           23.1884     C.
12  <000>  Horizon sensor                <       >
13  <000>  Spare (tbd)                   <       >
14  <026>  DCE RAMUNIT current           -6.6269     mA.
15  <064>  DCE CPU current               -61.5500    mA.
16  <695>  DCE GMEM current              273.1905    mA.
17  <470>  Facet temp +X                 2.0000      C.
.8  <452>  Facet temp +Y                 5.6000      C.
19  <613>  Facet temp +Z                 -26.6000    C.
20  <170>  Solar array current -X        657.4000    mA.
21  <080>  +10V line current             77.6000     mA.
22  <675>  PCM voltage +10V              10.1250     V.
23  <008>  P/W logic current (+5V)       1.1200      mA.
24  <009>  P/W Geiger current (+14V)     1.8900      mA.
25  <418>  P/W Elec sp.curr (+10V)       40.1280     mA.
26  <417>  P/W Elec sp.curr (-10V)       38.7810     mA.
27  <289>  Facet temp -X                 38.2000     C.
28  <480>  Facet temp -Y                 0.0000      C.
29  <458>  Facet temp -Z                 4.4000      C.
30  <290>  Solar array current +X        429.4000    mA.
31  <060>  -10V line current             28.8000     mA.
32  <665>  PCM voltage -10V              23.9400     V.
33  <240>  1802 comp curr (+10V)         50.4000     mA.
34  <011>  Digitalker current (+5V)      1.4300      mA.
35  <342>  145MHz beacon Power O/P       580.0000    mW.
36  <385>  145MHz beacon current         84.7000     mA.
.7  <395>  145MHz beacon temp            17.0000     C.
38  <488>  Command decoder temp (+Y)     -1.6000     C.
39  <522>  Telemetry temp (+X)           -8.4000     C.
40  <090>  Solar array voltage (+30V)    -42.6000    V.
41  <180>  +5V line current              174.6000    mA.
42  <726>  PCM voltage +5V               6.0984      V.
43  <175>  DSR current (+5V)             36.7500     mA.
44  <042>  Command RX current            38.6400     mA.
45  <000>  435MHz beacon Power O/P       -200.0000   mW.
46  <004>  435MHz beacon current         1.7600      mA.
47  <461>  435MHz beacon temp            3.8000      C.
48  <503>  P/W temp (-X)                 -4.6000     C.
49  <495>  BCR temp (-Y)                 -3.0000     C.
50  <080>  Battery charge/disch9 curr    -3810.4000  mA.
51  <100>  +14V line current             500.0000    mA.
52  <277>  Battery voltage (+14V)        5.8170      V.
53  <852>  Battery cell volts (MUX)      <       >
54  <169>  Telemetry current (+10V)      3.3800      mA.
55  <302>  2.4GHz beacon Power O/P       258.1333    mW.
56  <013>  2.4GHz beacon current         5.8500      mA.
57  <478>  Battery temp                  0.4000      C.
58  <477>  2.4GHz beacon temp            0.6000      C.
59  <488>  CCD imager temp               -1.6000     C.
```

FIG. 7.7   UoSAT–2 TELEMETRY

```
Source file: 'P.UOSAT11'

FRAME No.      : 00000000R000    (1)
Mission time   : 00/00/00        00:R0:00
AOS date/time  : 01/06/87        00:00 hrs.

Channels 00-69 telemetry
00 100  01 070  02 742  03 000  04 000  05 338  06 ---  07 461  08 474  09 314
10 140  11 250  12 000  13 000  14 026  15 162  16 642  17 488  18 452  19 ---
20 170  21 080  22 675  23 008  24 009  25 418  26 433  27 275  28 480  29 465
30 290  31 060  32 665  33 242  34 011  35 342  36 385  37 395  38 488  39 519
40 090  41 180  42 726  43 172  44 042  45 000  46 004  47 461  48 504  49 495
50 080  51 100  52 277  53 863  54 168  55 305  56 013  57 478  58 477  59 488
60 ---  61 ---  62 ---  63 ---  64 ---  65 ---  66 ---  67 ---  68 ---  69 ---

FRAME No.      : 8705310194108   (2)
Mission time   : 31/05/87        19:41:08
AOS date/time  : 01/06/87        00:00 hrs.

Channels 00-69 telemetry
00 100  01 070  02 742  03 000  04 000  05 338  06 211  07 461  08 474  09 314
10 140  11 250  12 000  13 008  14 026  15 162  16 642  17 488  18 452  19 612
20 170  21 080  22 675  23 008  24 009  25 418  26 433  27 275  28 480  29 465
30 290  31 060  32 665  33 242  34 011  35 000  36 385  37 395  38 488  39 519
40 090  41 180  42 726  43 ---  44 ---  45 000  46 004  47 461  48 504  49 495
50 ---  51 100  52 277  53 863  54 168  55 305  56 013  57 478  58 477  59 488
60 ---  61 ---  62 ---  63 ---  64 ---  65 ---  66 ---  67 ---  68 ---  69 ---
```

FIG. 7.8 UoSAT-2 NUMERIC TELEMETRY

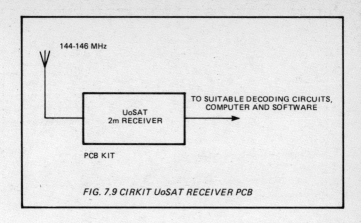

144-146 MHz

UoSAT
2m RECEIVER

TO SUITABLE DECODING CIRCUITS,
COMPUTER AND SOFTWARE

PCB KIT

*FIG. 7.9 CIRKIT UoSAT RECEIVER PCB*

# Chapter 8

# A NOAA GROUND STATION

This chapter describes the weather satellite receiving system from Unilab. As with the UoSAT systems it is designed for use with the BBC B, B+ or Master 128 micros. In addition, a monitor (colour if possible), printer (Epson preferably), disk drive and cassette recorder are required.

### The NOAA Satellite Series

This series of weather satellites, which are also known as TIROS (Television Infra-Red Orbital Satellites) transmit weather pictures at 120 lines per minute. The two satellites accessible by the Unilab system are the NOAA-9 and NOAA-10. These transmit signals at 137.62MHz and 137.5MHz respectively. (NOAA stands for National Oceanic and Atmospheric Administration.)

Both a visible and an infra-red image is provided of the earth's surface which is being overflown by the satellite. The NOAA satellite carries out polar orbits giving two sets (every twelve hours) of 3–4 usable passes per day.

The area covered (and receivable in Britain) extends from Greenland to the Mediterranean and from the Mid-Atlantic to the Urals.

The NOAA satellites carry out polar orbits which means that they travel from the South Pole to the North Pole over Britain (when overhead) and as each complete orbit takes about 100 minutes, then about 15 orbits occur every 24 hours. As the earth rotates (anti-clockwise) each orbital path must shift by 360 degrees/15 = 24 degrees. In other words, each pass is effectively 24 degrees west of the previous one. At certain times during the twenty-four hour period, the NOAA satellite may not be in a convenient reception position, regardless of what picture it is taking! Generally speaking, NOAA-9 provides about five usable passes during each 24 hours, and NOAA-10 5 or 6.

## Unilab System Outline

The NOAA Weather Satellite Ground Station package is detailed as follows:

Weather Satellite Receiver, with leads
Weather Picture Interface, with leads
Satellite Antenna, with phasing harness
Coaxial cable, 10 metres with connectors
WEATHER-PACK1 Picture software (40T disc, sample cassette tape, manual)
SAT-PACK-1 Orbit Prediction Software (40T disc, manual)
Schools Satellite Project Master Manual.

Apart from the BBC Micro System (detailed later) everything required for a fully operational ground station is provided.

Figures 8.1 and 8.2 detail automatic reception and loading of picture signals.

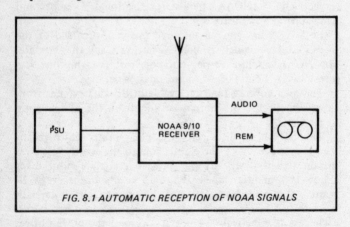

*FIG. 8.1 AUTOMATIC RECEPTION OF NOAA SIGNALS*

### Aerial

The aerial is described as a right-hand circularly polarised 'turnstile' antenna which consists of a pair of crossed loop dipoles and a pair of crossed reflectors. This aerial is omnidirectional and therefore does not need to be aimed at, or to

62

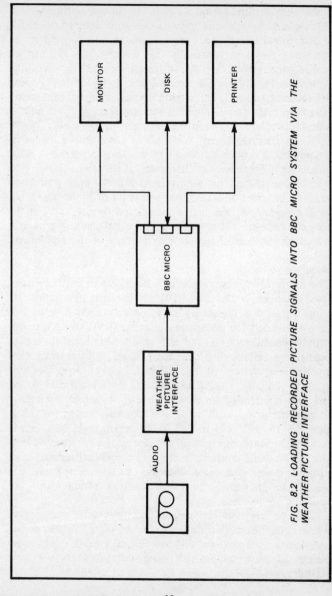

FIG. 8.2 LOADING RECORDED PICTURE SIGNALS INTO BBC MICRO SYSTEM VIA THE WEATHER PICTURE INTERFACE

track the satellite during its pass. Although optimum positioning may be achieved from a permanent siting of the aerial, it is one less variable to worry about and also convenient for recording passes automatically (i.e. unattended). I obtained satisfactory results with the aerial positioned vertically.

Full instructions on assembling the aerial on to its boom and correct (phased) connection details are given, plus useful diagrams. All that is required is a small screwdriver and an adjustable spanner if mounting the aerial on to a mast.

As in Chapter 7, my 'installation' consisted of the aerial clamped to a broom handle which was then gripped in a Black and Decker Workmate in the centre of the lawn! Despite its weird appearance, this arrangement worked very well at an altitude of some 5–6 feet, but well clear of house and trees.

Ten metres of coax cable terminated by BNC plug at the receiver end- and N-type plug at the aerial end are provided, which is very useful for temporary trials of the equipment.

## Receiver

The receiver, with provision for selecting up to six frequencies (two equipped, NOAA-9 and 10) is in the form of a flat orange topped steel case measuring about 24cm X 13cm X 4cm. It is clearly labelled for connection of aerial (BNC socket), power supply (banana sockets) and a 75 ohm type tv aerial socket for connection to tape recorder (MIC) input. A 4mm jack socket enables connection to the REMote socket of a portable cassette recorder. Aerial and cassette leads are included. As the unit is intended for school lab use a bench power supply is assumed to be easily available. Another reason for this is that the 16–18V a.c. or d.c. supply input could be achieved using lamp batteries enabling the receiver to be operated outside without the constraints of mains supplies. Presumably an optional mains unit would increase the cost of the unit and also make it slightly heavier. Current requirements are typically 150mA.

The receiver unit includes an audio amplifier and speaker which enables monitoring of the satellite signal during (attended) recordings (or just listening to a pass). This audio output is also 'tapped off' and outputted to the tape recorder.

In addition to the volume control a squelch control can be used to adjust the signal level which will activate the receiver and also turn on the recorder.

A Doppler monitor output is provided for those interested in observing carrier frequency changes as the satellite progresses towards and past the ground station.

After connecting up the receiver to the aerial and tape recorder, the squelch is set to just turn off the recorder remotely. The unit is then left to record the next pass or passes, remembering to depress the record keys and also switching on the external power supply!

Unless in attendance, or having information about pass times (more on this later), the unit can be left on overnight or during the day. Also, unless experienced in interpreting infra-red pictures it is more useful to record signals during the daytime, as pictures taken at night will not usually be very useful!

Before embarking on the recording and then processing of received signals, it is a good strategy to familiarise yourself with the system using the program disk (WEATHER-PACK 1) and sample tape.

This is clearly explained in the Master Manual and also the booklet accompanying the disk.

*Note:* Receiving satellite signals does not require the operation of the computer system, unless it is required to receive and monitor live pictures. However, this is not very practical due to RF interference generated by the computer itself.

I will return to the use of software and the processing of received data after looking at the next part of the hardware, namely the Interface Unit.

**Weather Picture Interface**

The interface unit is another flat box which matches the receiver in size and appearance. It has a mains psu, coax input from cassette (EAR) output and a switch to select SYNC A (infra-red picture) or SYNC B (visible picture).

Adjustable controls are provided for offset and (amplifier) gain which enable the unit to be adjusted to suit the level originating from the cassette tape. Instructions and diagrams are provided in the software manual and also on screen. The **WEATHER-PACK** software, which is menu-driven, allows adjustment to be made via visual graphical information on screen. Once set, this should need no further adjustment. In my case the offset control was set to about 12 o'clock and the gain at about 9 o'clock.

Output from the interface is via ribbon cable to the BBC User Port.

The audio input to the interface unit is in analogue form. This can be listened to and produces a tick-tock sound, with tones between each tick and tock. The ticks and tocks are actually the sync pulses for each picture line, i.e. tick is sync pulse A (for infra-red) and the tock is sync pulse B (for visible). The tone signals in between are the picture line signals.

For more detail of waveforms refer back to Figures 5.2 and 5.3 and accompanying explanation in Chapter 5.

The purpose of the interface is to convert this analogue information into digital form which the micro can then display on screen by writing the appropriate grey scale values as individual pixels on the screen. Thus the interface is basically an A/D converter.

**WEATHER-PACK** software then produces a digital picture representation on the screen as it is read from cassette, via the A/D unit.

The picture is produced from the bottom of the screen one line at a time and takes about five minutes to complete. Completed pictures can be transferred to disk and afterwards rewritten to the screen, but this time much more quickly.

As before, no problems were encountered when using the interface unit. Connection is straightforward, all leads are supplied and the manuals give full instructions.

Trying out the interface unit and familiarising yourself with its operation is recommended using the sample tape to display a picture on screen and also to copy a picture from screen to disk. This makes it easier when dealing with your own recorded pictures.

The Unilab system is very easy to use, being well organised and documented. It represents quite a sophisticated system in terms of hardware and software and provides a great deal of scope for a relatively small outlay.

I found the equipment/system worked first time, with no problems, apart from familiarisation with the different aspects of receiving, decoding and displaying.

The most difficult part of operating the system is understanding what is happening in terms of satellite position, interpreting received pictures and knowing when to expect a useful pass. Although some information is given in the documentation, it must be realised that the Unilab system is a tool and the user must expect to learn and find out about the NOAA satellites from other sources.

## WEATHER-PACK 1

As the Unilab system is computer based, software is essential for the decoding of received picture signals. WEATHER-PACK 1 provides a suite of programs on one disc with facilities outlined as follows (SAT-PACK 1, the orbital prediction program is very useful but not as essential as the WEATHER-PACK 1 disc).

WEATHER-PACK 1 comprises the 5¼" 40T single sided disc with the following facilities:

Set Resolution
 — 8 shades, high resolution, 8 minutes of pass,
  half screen width (BBC Mode 1)
 — 8 shades, medium resolution, 4 minutes of pass, full
  screen width (BBC Mode 2)
Change default drive — enables single drive system to be
  used for program and data disc.
Set Sync Trigger — allows sync level to be set for best
  results from tape output.

A sample cassette tape with a received picture signal can be loaded into the BBC Micro via the interface unit and then displayed on the screen. The manual provides full instructions on how to drive the menu-driven software and a keystrip is also provided.

Adjust Interface — produces graphs of amplitude variations.
  Prompts show how to adjust 'offset' and 'gain' controls
  for best results.

New picture — enables picture signals stored on cassette to be loaded to screen.

Load picture — enables pictures stored on disk to be loaded to screen.

Merged pictures — two half width pictures can be placed side-by-side on the screen for comparison.

Set colours — different sets of 4 colours can be toggled for colour or monochrome VDUs.

Other facilities include screen to printer dump (printer screen dump program required). Also inversion of picture (i.e. N—S to S—N).

Display modes:
    Mode 1 (BBC 320 × 256)   4 colour
    Mode 2 (BBC 160 × 256) 16 colour   — (8 actually used)
    Printer dump routine — this is provided as WXDUMP on the disk if you are using an Epson compatible printer of the FX-80 type.

## Some Sample Results

The table in Figure 8.3 lists some typical results achieved. These results are based on a table which conveniently appeared in 'OSCAR NEWS' produced by AMSAT-UK.

Although this publication deals mainly with UoSAT satellites, GM3CEA from Stranraer had produced these prediction figures. Discrepancies in the times (i.e. earlier) are presumed to be due to the South—North travelling satellite passing over the vicinity of Hinckley in Leicestershire before reaching Stranraer!

L.EQX is the latitude position at which the NOAA satellite crosses the 0 degree longitude Equator in an approximate S—N direction.

Satellite crossings are usually stated as being between 0—360 deg. W, although maps use 0—180 deg. W (clockwise) and 0—180 deg. E (anti-clockwise). I have included both forms.

The table shows a total of six satellite passes, but most passes last for 10 minutes or more, and as it takes about five minutes to fill a screen, up to three 'screenfuls' may be achieved. It is even possible to dump these successively to a

| Satellite | GMT | L.EQX | Actual Time | Pass No. | Screen No. | Cassette Counter |
|---|---|---|---|---|---|---|
| NOAA-10 | 9.42 a.m. | 212W (148E) | 9.30 a.m. | 1 | 1<br>2<br>3 | 000<br>093<br>172 |
| NOAA-9 | 12.29 p.m. | 319W (41E) | 12.05 p.m. | 2 | 1 | 272 |
| NOAA-9 | 2.11 p.m. | 345W (15E) | 2.00 p.m. | 3 | 1<br>2 | 304<br>425 |
| NOAA-9 | 3.53 p.m. | 010W | 3.15 p.m. | 4 | 1<br>2 | 459<br>513 |
| NOAA-10 | 6.09 p.m. | 339W (21E) | 6.00 p.m. | 5 | 1<br>2 | 000<br>100 |
| NOAA-10 | 7.50 p.m. | 004W | 7.15 p.m. | 6 | 1<br>2<br>3<br>4 | 216<br>284<br>347<br>403 |

FIG. 8.3   RECEIVED SIGNALS RELATING TO NOAA-9/10 PREDICTIONS

69

printer and then join them up. Recording cassette counter numbers is useful for backtracking and tying in results with predictions.

These results (pictures) may require time and effort in interpretation, as you need to know the actual orbital path (not actually due North from its Equator passing point), whether it is in good radio range and depending on its elevation how long the pass is. It also helps to know which direction it is travelling! (It is possible to receive picture signals when it is heading over the North Pole in a southerly direction.) The complete prediction chart is shown in Figure 8.4 from which the simplified table was derived.

This is when the picture inversion facility is useful. Thus in theory you might get pictures from as far away as Japan, Turkey, etc. Poor visibility can also be a problem, and pictures over the Atlantic may not be easy to interpret!

### Technical Details

| | |
|---|---|
| NOAA altitude: | 800km |
| NOAA orbit time: | 101 minutes |
| RF carrier frequency: | NOAA-9 — 137.62MHz |
| | NOAA-10 — 137.5MHz |
| Tone: | sub-carrier signal of frequency 2400Hz |

Amplitude represents bright and dark areas.

After sync pulse, picture line is transmitted as a one-quarter second burst of modulated sub-carrier (tone).

Each line is 600 cycles of sub-carrier.

A/D converter is 8-bit device, which provides for 256 different shades. The BBC micro modes provide only 4 ranges (Mode 1) or 8 (Mode 2).

Minute markers are displayed on screen which not only relate to the pass time and therefore the displayed picture, but are useful when comparing (or 'synchronising') visible and infra-red screen or printer pictures.

Software provision for labelling picture files before saving to disk, e.g. latitude, satellite type, etc.

IR black — warm, white — cold.

Channel 1 (visible) 7 sync pulses at 1040 pulses per sec.
Channel 1 (infra-red) 7 sync pulses at 832 pulses per sec.

# SATURDAY PREDICTIONS for NOAA 9/10 – GM3CEA

NOAA-9 SATELLITE. – APT.137.62 MHz.

REF. ORBIT NUMBER     11886
REF. DAY, MONTH, YEAR   4, 4, 87
REF. G.M.T.  H,M,S   00,54,29,745
REF. LONG. EQX. DEGS.  141.35941

| DATE | ORBIT. | G.M.T. | L.EQX |
|------|--------|--------|-------|
| 09:05:87 | 12381 | 02:42:18 | 173 |
| 09:05:87 | 12382 | 04:24:23 | 198 |
| 09:05:87 | 12387 | 12:54:46 | 326 |
| 09:05:87 | 12388 | 14:36:50 | 351 |
| 09:05:87 | 12389 | 16:18:55 | 017 |
| 16:05:87 | 12480 | 03:07:52 | 179 |
| 16:05:87 | 12481 | 04:49:56 | 204 |
| 16:05:87 | 12486 | 13:20:19 | 332 |
| 16:05:87 | 12487 | 15:02:24 | 358 |
| 16:05:87 | 12488 | 16:44:29 | 023 |
| 23:05:87 | 12579 | 03:33:26 | 185 |
| 23:05:87 | 12584 | 12:03:48 | 313 |
| 23:05:87 | 12585 | 13:45:53 | 338 |
| 23:05:87 | 12586 | 15:27:58 | 004 |
| 30:05:87 | 12677 | 02:16:55 | 166 |
| 30:05:87 | 12678 | 03:58:59 | 191 |
| 30:05:87 | 12683 | 12:29:22 | 319 |
| 30:05:87 | 12684 | 14:11:27 | 345 |
| 30:05:87 | 12685 | 15:53:31 | 010 |
| 06:06:87 | 12776 | 02:42:28 | 172 |
| 06:06:87 | 12777 | 04:24:33 | 198 |
| 06:06:87 | 12782 | 12:54:56 | 325 |
| 06:06:87 | 12783 | 14:37:00 | 351 |
| 06:06:87 | 12784 | 16:19:05 | 016 |
| 13:06:87 | 12875 | 03:08:02 | 178 |
| 13:06:87 | 12876 | 04:50:07 | 204 |
| 13:06:87 | 12881 | 13:20:29 | 332 |
| 13:06:87 | 12882 | 15:02:34 | 357 |
| 13:06:87 | 12883 | 16:44:39 | 023 |
| 20:06:87 | 12974 | 03:33:36 | 185 |
| 20:06:87 | 12979 | 12:03:59 | 312 |
| 20:06:87 | 12980 | 13:46:03 | 338 |
| 20:06:87 | 12981 | 15:28:08 | 003 |
| 27:06:87 | 13072 | 02:17:05 | 165 |
| 27:06:87 | 13073 | 03:59:09 | 191 |
| 27:06:87 | 13078 | 12:29:32 | 318 |
| 27:06:87 | 13079 | 14:11:37 | 344 |
| 27:06:87 | 13080 | 15:53:41 | 010 |
| 04:07:87 | 13171 | 02:42:38 | 172 |
| 04:07:87 | 13172 | 04:24:43 | 197 |
| 04:07:87 | 13177 | 12:55:06 | 325 |
| 04:07:87 | 13178 | 14:37:11 | 350 |
| 04:07:87 | 13179 | 16:19:15 | 016 |

NODAL PERIOD......1:42:04
LONG. INCREMENT......25.51

DAILY CHANGE.  Earlier By:-
GMT 10min.55sec. L-EQX 2.7Degs.

DATA FOR AMSAT-UK AZEL PROGRAM.
PERIOD....MINS. 102.0766
INCLINATION.... 99.04415

NOTE:- Predictions are for Saturdays.
Apply DAILY CHANGE to compute
orbits for other days.

NOAA-10 SATELLITE. – APT.137.50 MHz.

REF. ORBIT NUMBER     2821
REF. DAY, MONTH, YEAR   4, 4, 87
REF. G.M.T.  H,M,S   01,31,21,609
REF. LONG. EQX. DEGS.  89.33027

| DATE | ORBIT. | G.M.T. | L.EQX |
|------|--------|--------|-------|
| 09:05:87 | 3322 | 07:16:29 | 176 |
| 09:05:87 | 3323 | 08:57:46 | 201 |
| 09:05:87 | 3324 | 10:39:03 | 226 |
| 09:05:87 | 3328 | 17:24:12 | 327 |
| 09:05:87 | 3329 | 19:05:29 | 352 |
| 09:05:87 | 3330 | 20:46:47 | 018 |
| 16:05:87 | 3421 | 06:23:57 | 162 |
| 16:05:87 | 3422 | 08:05:15 | 188 |
| 16:05:87 | 3423 | 09:46:32 | 213 |
| 16:05:87 | 3428 | 18:12:58 | 340 |
| 16:05:87 | 3429 | 19:54:15 | 005 |
| 23:05:87 | 3521 | 07:12:43 | 175 |
| 23:05:87 | 3522 | 08:54:01 | 200 |
| 23:05:87 | 3523 | 10:35:18 | 225 |
| 23:05:87 | 3527 | 17:20:27 | 327 |
| 23:05:87 | 3528 | 19:01:44 | 352 |
| 23:05:87 | 3529 | 20:43:02 | 017 |
| 30:05:87 | 3620 | 06:20:12 | 161 |
| 30:05:87 | 3621 | 08:01:30 | 187 |
| 30:05:87 | 3622 | 09:42:47 | 212 |
| 30:05:87 | 3627 | 18:09:13 | 339 |
| 30:05:87 | 3628 | 19:50:30 | 004 |
| 06:06:87 | 3720 | 07:08:58 | 174 |
| 06:06:87 | 3721 | 08:50:16 | 199 |
| 06:06:87 | 3722 | 10:31:33 | 224 |
| 06:06:87 | 3726 | 17:16:42 | 326 |
| 06:06:87 | 3727 | 18:57:59 | 351 |
| 06:06:87 | 3728 | 20:39:16 | 016 |
| 13:06:87 | 3819 | 06:16:27 | 160 |
| 13:06:87 | 3820 | 07:57:44 | 186 |
| 13:06:87 | 3821 | 09:39:02 | 211 |
| 13:06:87 | 3826 | 18:05:28 | 338 |
| 13:06:87 | 3827 | 19:46:45 | 003 |
| 20:06:87 | 3919 | 07:05:13 | 173 |
| 20:06:87 | 3920 | 08:46:30 | 198 |
| 20:06:87 | 3921 | 10:27:48 | 223 |
| 20:06:87 | 3925 | 17:12:57 | 325 |
| 20:06:87 | 3926 | 18:54:14 | 350 |
| 20:06:87 | 3927 | 20:35:31 | 015 |
| 27:06:87 | 4018 | 06:12:42 | 160 |
| 27:06:87 | 4019 | 07:53:59 | 185 |
| 27:06:87 | 4020 | 09:35:17 | 210 |
| 27:06:87 | 4025 | 18:01:43 | 337 |
| 27:06:87 | 4026 | 19:43:00 | 002 |
| 04:07:87 | 4118 | 07:01:28 | 172 |
| 04:07:87 | 4119 | 08:42:45 | 197 |
| 04:07:87 | 4120 | 10:24:03 | 222 |
| 04:07:87 | 4124 | 17:09:12 | 324 |
| 04:07:87 | 4125 | 18:50:29 | 349 |
| 04:07:87 | 4126 | 20:31:46 | 014 |

NODAL PERIOD......1:41:17
LONG. INCREMENT......25.32

DAILY CHANGE.  Earlier By:-
GMT 21min.58sec. L-EQX 5.4Degs.

DATA FOR AMSAT-UK AZEL PROGRAM.
PERIOD....MINS. 101.2879
INCLINATION.... 98.72172

GM3CEA - STRANRAER.

*FIG. 8.4   COMPLETE PREDICTION CHART FOR NOAA9/10*
*(reproduced by permission of AMSAT-UK)*

Modulation: 5% black — 80% white.
Resolution: Mode 1 — 320 × 256 = 81,920 pixels
Mode 2 — 160 × 256 = 40,960 pixels.

These figures compare favourably with more costly systems having typical resolutions of 256 × 256 × 16 = 10,485,576 pixels. Obviously the more pixels (picture elements) the more detail in the picture.

## Conclusions

Most people find the idea of receiving satellite weather pictures quite interesting, as they can relate it to something which affects them (the weather) and are also familiar with weather forecasting by this means on national television.

Schools and hobbyists tend to find the subject fascinating and are keen to find out more once they have witnessed a demonstration.

The Unilab NOAA receiving system provides a sound basis in terms of hardware and software for investigating this area in some considerable detail.

As a complete system (aerial, receiver, interface, software and documentation) it provides a fairly sophisticated system which is relatively easy to install and commission. Although the system represents a great deal of time and effort and the utilisation of experience from many sources, it still provides an incentive to learn more about the subject and also a source of continued stimulation and intellectual challenge.

In a nutshell, the Unilab system represents good value for money and a good starting point for school or college project work. The equipment is reliable and produces good results. It also compares favourably with more expensive systems, including METEOSAT.

## Cirkit Weather Satellite System

VHF Weather Satellite receiver (kit):

This is a six-channel, crystal controlled receiver, suitable for receiving NOAA-8 and NOAA-9 signals and also Russian and American satellites. An interface and software (also available from Cirkit) is also needed (and an aerial!). It is supplied with one channel equipped, at 137.5MHz.

Weather Satellite Interface (kit):

This converts the analogue signal from the receiver into a digital signal suitable for the user port of the BBC Micro (the sync pulse is input via the printer port).

SATPIC:

A ROM based software package for the BBC B Micro. Provides displays for NOAA visible and infra-red transmission, Russian weather satellites and Meteosat 2. Other facilities include zoom mode to display British Isles.

A block diagram of the complete system is shown in Figure 8.5.

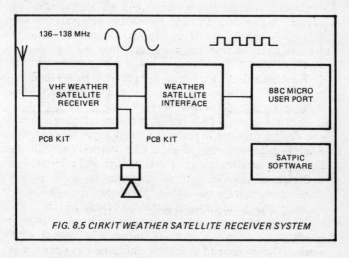

FIG. 8.5 CIRKIT WEATHER SATELLITE RECEIVER SYSTEM

**Maplin Weather Satellite Receiving System**

Comprising:

    Receiver (pre-assembled PCB module)

    or

    Sat Receiver Kit

    Aerial or Sat Aerial Kit

    Decoder (comprising 3 PCBs) or Decoder in kit form

    Down Converter (separate modules)

    or

Down Converter, Pre-Amp and Aerial Kit.

*Note:* The Down Converter is to enable Meteosat signals to be received (refer to Chapter 9).

Other associated items available are a VHF pre-amplifier module and a frame store based on a Z80 controller. (The latter provides an alternative to using a home computer and provides a higher resolution display.)

A block diagram of the basic Maplin NOAA system is shown in Figure 8.6.

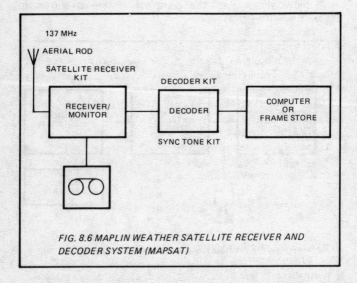

FIG. 8.6 MAPLIN WEATHER SATELLITE RECEIVER AND DECODER SYSTEM (MAPSAT)

For further comprehensive details refer to Maplin catalogue (address in Appendix 2).

# Chapter 9

# A METEOSAT GROUND STATION

A system for receiving Meteosat signals is available from Timestep Electronics. It is basically a NOAA system used in conjunction with the BBC Micro but having the option of a Meteosat frequency converter unit and dish aerial.

## Timestep Electronics System

The system is comprised as follows:

    NOAA active aerial with 35m cable

    10-channel receiver fitted with 137.3, 137.5 and 137.62 MHz crystals (remaining slots for expansion)

    Interface

    3-mode colour software SATPIC ROM (BBC Master compatible)

    Demonstration disk showing NOAA and Meteosat pictures

    Demonstration tape of satellite passes

    All plugs and leads

    Installation and operating manual.

Figure 9.1 shows the Timestep system.

## Meteosat Dish and Converter

The 0.9m dish aerial is suitable for wall or roof mounting, requiring a clear line of sight due south at 30 degrees elevation. An alternative is for it to be set up on a portable frame. The converter can be up to 10m from the dish and needs to be indoors.

The Meteosat dish is claimed to give access to 24 hours a day of visible and infra-red pictures of almost half the globe with close-ups of the European and Atlantic region twice every hour.

A range of software is available which provides such features as radio footprints of all weather satellites and UoSATs, image interpretation and map overlays.

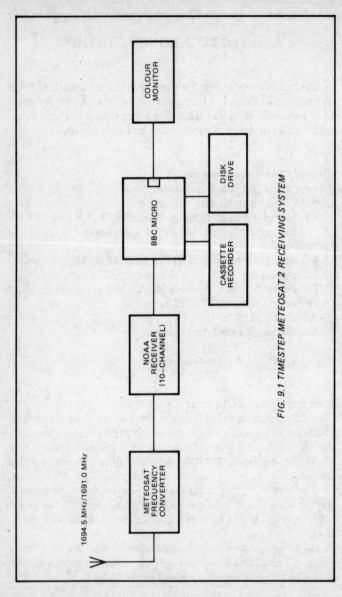

1694.5 MHz/1691.0 MHz

COLOUR MONITOR

BBC MICRO

DISK DRIVE

CASSETTE RECORDER

NOAA RECEIVER (10–CHANNEL)

METEOSAT FREQUENCY CONVERTER

*FIG. 9.1 TIMESTEP METEOSAT 2 RECEIVING SYSTEM*

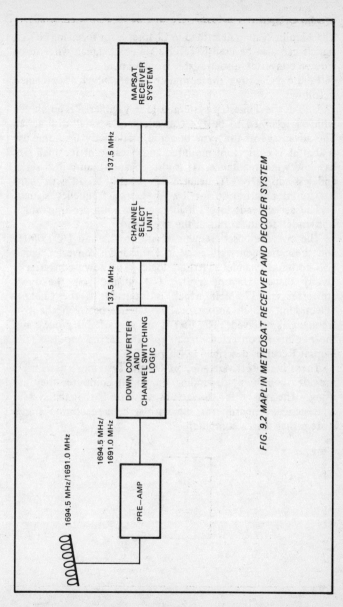

FIG. 9.2 MAPLIN METEOSAT RECEIVER AND DECODER SYSTEM

77

## Maplin System

The Maplin system described in Chapter 8 for receiving NOAA signals can also be used to receive Meteosat signals when using a down converter, also available from Maplin.

Figure 9.2 shows the complete system which is explained as follows.

Unlike the Timestep system, a loop-yagi aerial is employed which is claimed to be the equivalent of a small dish aerial. The advantage of this type of aerial particularly for home use is that it is easily roof mounted and because of its small size has low wind resistance. It is also cheaper than a dish aerial and less unsightly. Its beam width is fairly broad with sharp horizontal polarisation for low level, high frequency signals.

The aerial feeds into a high gain low noise pre-amp which is intended for mounting at the mast head.

The two Meteosat frequencies are 1694.5 and 1691.0MHz and these frequencies are fed into the down converter which also contains channel switching logic. The down converter is ideally placed at roof level. The output from the down converter is 137.5MHz which is inputted to the Channel Select Unit which automatically switches between the two frequencies received. The user is unaware of this process and the required converted signal appears at the input of the Mapsat Receiver described in Chapter 8.

There is no software support for this system, so users must provide their own, depending on which computer they are using. The reason for the lack of software is that the system is designed primarily for use with a high resolution frame store rather than a computer.

# Chapter 10

# THE UNIVERSITY OF SURREY SPACECRAFT ENGINEERING RESEARCH UNIT

In this penultimate but last major chapter, it is appropriate to look again at an organisation which has established itself as a world leader in the development of amateur satellites via the highly successful UoSAT-1 and UoSAT-2 experimental satellites designed, built and operated in orbit by the UoSAT team at Surrey University. An awareness of the vast range of sophisticated scientific and technological facilities provided by UoSATs is useful if not actually essential to the reader/user.

The University of Surrey Spacecraft Engineering Research Unit is located within the Department of Electronic and Electrical Engineering and provides a national focus for research into satellite engineering topics with a particular emphasis on advanced yet low cost solutions.

The Research Unit provides expertise in spacecraft design, construction, test, integration and orbital operation and the appropriate resources.

Research and industrial projects are undertaken either by the Research Unit or the limited company formed under the title of Surrey Satellite Technology Limited (SST). Typical projects undertaken include mission strategies, hardware and software design, space-qualified hardware fabrication, assembly and test, spacecraft design and orbital operations.

SST was founded in 1985 by the University in partnership with General Technology Systems, to provide a professional interface between the university and industry to enable efficient technology transfer and commercial development of the on-going research and to undertake industrial contracts.

The low cost spacecraft techniques developed by SST have direct applications in:

Technology test-bed/proving flights
Communication
Navigation

79

Imaging
Space science
Space education

In a way it is almost amusing to think that a part of an electronic engineering department in a British university is operating like a mini-NASA (but without the launch facilities!). The Research Unit does actually collaborate with NASA, ESA, AMSAT and other agencies worldwide.

## UoSAT-1 and UoSAT-2

These two satellites (UoSAT-1 now decayed) were designed and built at University of Surrey. (As mentioned in Chapter 4, UoSAT's demise in October 1989 has effectively been countered by BRAMSAT's DOVE microsatellite launched in January 1990 and operating on the same frequency, i.e. 148.125MHz). UoSAT-3 was also launched at the same time.

UoSAT-1 was launched into a 500km orbit into a sun-synchronous, polar earth orbit by NASA-DELTA on 6th October 1981. Its mission objectives were stated as being:

(1) To investigate the problems associated with low cost yet sophisticated spacecraft.
(2) To evaluate new technologies and cost-effective design philosophies in orbit.
(3) To stimulate space education through direct participation.

It is estimated that signals from UoSAT-1 were received by some 3000 experimenters worldwide.

UoSAT-2 was launched on 1st March 1984 by NASA-DELTA into a 700km orbit. Improved cost-effective design features included are as follows:

(1) Advanced gravity-gradient stabilisation.
(2) Autonomous spacecraft operation using the spacecraft on-board computer.
(3) Store-and-forward digital communications.
(4) Medium resolution CCD earth imaging.
(5) Space radiation environment monitoring.

(6)   Space education experiments — DIGITALKER synthesised speech, personal computer-compatible data transmission.

## UoSAT Mission Control Centre
In addition to tracking and communicating with UoSATs the ground station (Mission Control Centre) also tracks NOAA, METEOR, METEOSAT and other satellites.

A network of computers, including many BBC Micros enables a wide range of digital data from the spacecraft to be received and displayed in real time whilst being archived on the university's mainframe computers enabling more detailed analysis to be performed off-line.

## Research Funding
Research studies in the UoSAT Spacecraft Engineering Unit are supported by the SERC (Science and Research Council) through research grants and industry through research contracts. The Research Unit is involved with all aspects of advanced spacecraft engineering including:

Advanced spacecraft power systems
On-board computers and data handling networks
Modulation/demodulation schemes for satellite
   communication
Radiation frequency transmitter/receivers
Signal processing
Spacecraft attitude determination, stabilisation and
   control
Imaging
Space radiation effects on spacecraft components
Store-and-forward communication techniques from low
   earth orbiting satellites
Custom VLSI sub-system design
Failure resilient architecture.

## UoSAT Digital Communication (DCE)
Store-and-forward communications are supported by the DCE on UoSAT-2. The DCE exploits the fact that a low,

polar-orbiting satellite comes within range of every point on the earth several times every day. Thus one low cost spacecraft can provide global coverage for small, simple ground stations.

## Attitude Determination, Control and Stabilisation
Low cost digital sensors for sun, earth horizon and geomagnetic fields are designed and built at Surrey. Complex control algorithms executed by the on-board computer (OBC) aiming to achieve precise earth pointing.

## Advanced VLSI On-Board Data Handling Microcircuits
Custom VLSI (Very Large Scale Integration) 'gate array' microcircuits have been designed by the Research Unit to provide telemetry and telecommunications functions. Dramatic savings in volume and mass are made within these ICs.

## UK Technology Satellite (T-SAT)
The Research Unit plays a prime role in a UK Technology Spacecraft study (T-SAT) sponsored by SERC. Destined for a high elliptical earth orbit, the spacecraft aims to:

(1) Stimulate space technology and training within the UK university community.
(2) Conduct a design study for a technology demonstrator spacecraft to enhance the state-of-the-art of UK space engineering.

Figure 10.1 shows the T-SAT orbit, which is very different to a UoSAT orbit, having an apogee of 39,000km and a perigee of 1000km. The geostationary orbit in the diagram is for comparison only and although drawn as an ellipse for perspective, is actually a circular orbit.

Surrey University's contribution to the study is to create innovative designs for the following sub-systems:

Power
Telemetry and telecommand
On-board computing and data handling.

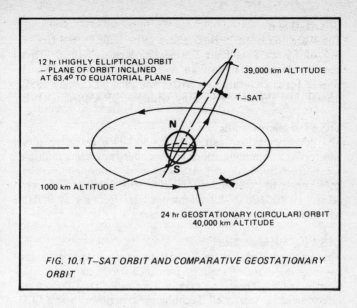

*FIG. 10.1 T–SAT ORBIT AND COMPARATIVE GEOSTATIONARY ORBIT*

In addition, Surrey has studied and is proposing the following technology demonstration payloads for T-SAT:

Fibre-optic data bus
Earth imaging experiment
Radio amateur communications payload.

## Research Facilities

The UoSAT Research Unit comprises 25 research staff located within four dedicated laboratories and five offices, supported by extensive technical, secretarial, computer and communications services.

In addition to the features typically provided by a university research department, the Research Unit has a spacecraft assembly Clean Room featuring a filtered air supply and protective clothing. Software and development laboratories are also provided.

## UoSAT-D & E

These are the latest microsatellites to be built by the University of Surrey Spacecraft Engineering Research Unit. They were mounted on top of an ARIANE-40 rocket in French Guiana for launch into low earth orbit on 22nd January 1990, where they shared the journey with the BRAMSAT DOVE.

## UoSAT-D Microsatellite

The primary payload carried by UoSAT-D is a digital store-and-forward communications transponder supporting multiple access from hundreds of portable ground stations and particularly suited to communications in remote or disaster-stricken areas. A 80C186 16-bit microcontroller (running at 8MHz) will be tested in space for the first time.

## UoSAT-E Microsatellite

This satellite carries three in-orbit technology demonstration payloads to evaluate their performance over extended operation in space. These comprise a Transputer Data Processing Experiment, a Solar Cell Technology experiment and a CCD (charge coupled device) Earth Imaging Camera.

The UoSAT-D and UoSAT-E spacecraft each measure 345 X 345 X 600mm with a mass of 45kg. The total mission budget for both spacecraft is £700 000. They became UoSAT-3 and UoSAT-4 upon successful injection into orbit.

## UoSAT Modular Microsatellite Bus

UoSAT-D and UoSAT-E (3 and 4) are the first missions to use the novel, modular microsatellite bus developed at Surrey and providing a highly adaptable spacecraft platform which enables a rapid response to individual launch opportunities into a variety of orbits. Figure 10.2 details the UoSAT-D configuration and also stabilisation boom, to scale.

Figure 10.3 gives details of 'tray' contents of UoSAT-D and UoSAT-E.

As can be seen in Figure 10.3, both satellites use identical housekeeping modules, providing the basic satellite functions, onto which the different payloads have been integrated. Each module comprises a standardised 'tray' which contains the electronic circuits. The satellite is built by standing these trays

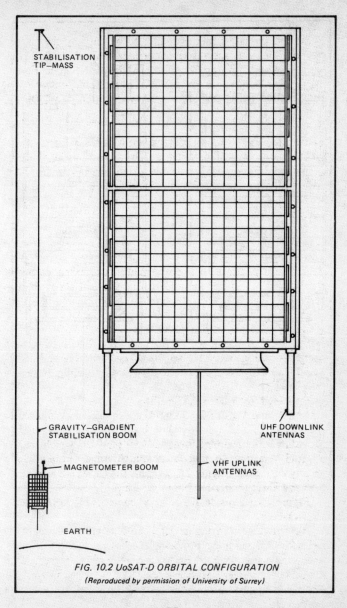

STABILISATION TIP—MASS

GRAVITY—GRADIENT STABILISATION BOOM

MAGNETOMETER BOOM

UHF DOWNLINK ANTENNAS

VHF UPLINK ANTENNAS

EARTH

*FIG. 10.2 UoSAT-D ORBITAL CONFIGURATION*
*(Reproduced by permission of University of Surrey)*

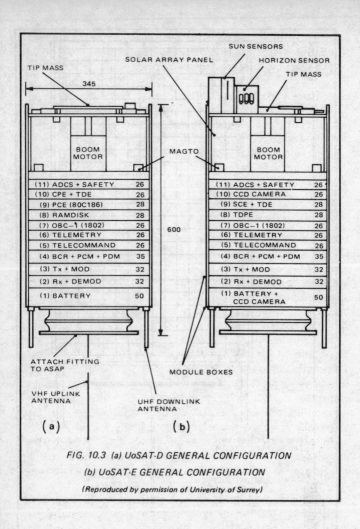

*FIG. 10.3 (a) UoSAT-D GENERAL CONFIGURATION*

*(b) UoSAT-E GENERAL CONFIGURATION*

*(Reproduced by permission of University of Surrey)*

together to form the basic structure. Solar cell panels are then
fitted to this structure to provide electrical power.

The basic modules are detailed below:

Battery Module
Downlink Transmitter and Modulator Module
Uplink Receiver and Demodulator Module
Power Conditioning Module
Telemetry and Telecommand Module
On-board Computer Module
Attitude Determination, Control and Strategy Module
Magnetometer Module.

## UoSAT-4 Status

UoSAT-3 and UoSAT-4 were launched successfully in January
1990 and operated correctly after launch. However, after 30
hours of operation UoSAT-4 fell silent! Unfortunately, it is
now considered as being 'written off' as it is only semi-
operational, with only its local oscillator being detected by
American users.

## The Future of Amateur Satellite Communications

The continuing research and development work carried out by
UoSAT will provide amateur and educational users with a
permanent source of satellite activities using the latest
engineering, radio and digital electronics techniques, for the
foreseeable future. Readers of this book will realise that
satellite tracking and receiving of signals requires a working
knowledge of the craft themselves, their facilities, where-
abouts and an ability to use suitable receiving and decoding
systems.

Satellite work at hobbyist or educational level is a complex
activity but need not be complicated. This book and those
listed in Appendix 3 will hopefully inspire current and aspiring
enthusiasts to learn about satellites in orbit, space in the
vicinity of the earth and be able to participate in the associated current, on-going and future technological advances.

## Chapter 11

# RECEIVING, DECODING AND PROCESSING EQUIPMENT – PRESENT AND FUTURE DEVELOPMENTS

In previous chapters examples of suitable systems for receiving signals from UoSAT, NOAA and Meteosat satellites have been described, some in great detail.

No price information has been provided as it is unlikely that this would be accurate at the time of publication of this book. The suppliers mentioned are not necessarily recommended by the author, but would not have been included if they were unreliable in use or difficult to operate. A typical system is unlikely to be bought for less than £200 although constructing individual boards from kits could save money.

The following pages give additional information and recent and proposed developments in respect of receiving, decoding and processing satellite signals. One of the aims of the book has been to describe the satellite systems themselves and it may be obvious that keeping up with developments (e.g. new launches) and knowing when a satellite is malfunctioning or has 'burnt up' is important. Equally important is knowing how to obtain suitable ground station equipment and be able to maintain it in terms of hardware and software updates.

One encouraging aspect of satellite tracking for the amateur is that there is a great deal of financial investment in orbit and a great deal of expertise including available tracking aids in existence. This, coupled with reliable home computers such as the Acorn range and the expanding PC market make this particularly fascinating hobby more than just a passing phase.

**Unilab**
Unilab equipment described in Chapters 7 and 8 is still at the time of writing available (after over four years) and according to their sales department unlikely to be terminated in the foreseeable future. Product development details are as follows.

## NOAA Systems

Systems are currently available for the BBC Micro and the Archimedes A300, A400 and A3000 computers. The BBC Weather Picture Interface for the BBC Micro is also compatible with the Archimedes. The Archimedes computer needs to be fitted with the I/O module/expansion card so that a BBC-like user port is available. A special interfacing box for the A3000 will be produced by Unilab at the end of 1990. This will provide printer, 1MHz bus and analogue ports as on the BBC Micro.

BBC users upgrading to the Archimedes need only change their software. Weather satellite picture software is currently available and an Archimedes version of the tracking software is in preparation.

## Weather Satellite Software

Unilab claim that the Archimedes produces pictures which can have a ground resolution of less than 10km and can be smoothly scrolled up and down the screen. The software is described as being able 'to use the power of the Archimedes to interpret more satellite data than has been previously possible in schools'. It produces displays with sixty-four grey scales (requiring a black and white monitor). Details such as ice flows around Greenland, mountains, rivers and lakes in Europe can be seen.

WEATHER-PACK II enables a BBC Micro user to obtain much higher resolution from captured NOAA picture signals. The computer is also used to enhance images by processing data from the satellite prior to display.

Although Unilab have a definite commitment to Acorn computers due to their continued presence in the educational and hobbyist markets they are working on software which will run the same satellite equipment with PC (IBM compatible) computers. Hardware is completed, but software should be available by the end of 1990.

## UoSAT Systems

No change with basic Unilab system and no plans at present for an Archimedes version although this is being considered

A very slight modification to the UoSAT Data Demodulator and a different computer connection cable enables the system to run from PC software available from Surrey University.

## Maplin

The full Mapsat system as described in detail in the Maplin catalogue is still available and likely to continue to be. There have been some improvements made to the hardware and improvements under development are as follows:

Additional kit for aerial

Improved pre-amp (as a result of weaker satellite signals and interference in some areas from cellphones)

Automatic picture synchronising devices

Mark 2 version of power supply

Swapping over of Channels A and B, as per Meteosat

Anticipation of new Meteosat launch in 1991

Auto tuning (synthesised) modification to Mapsat receiver.

Maplin do not market software, as their system is biased towards the use of a frame store rather than a computer. The Acorn, PC and other machines are only a realistic proposition if the user is prepared to write his or her own software.

# Appendix 1

## USEFUL ADDRESSES

Professor Martin Sweeting,
Director of Satellite Engineering/
Technical Director SST
Senate House
University of Surrey
Guildford
Surrey GU2 5XH

*Also:* Mr Craig Underwood
Research Fellow (Radiation Studies)
Tel: 0483 509143

Mr R. J. C. Broadbent, G3AAJ
AMSAT-UK
94 Herongate Road
Wanstead Park
London E12 5EQ
Tel: 081-989 6741

C5 SASE required for enquiries on membership or general information, please.

**DOVE Project:**
Dr Junior Torres de Castro
**AMSAT-BRAZIL** Presidente
Rue Macaubal 119
CEP 01256
Sao Paulo
SP Brazil

Mr Richard E. Ensign,
Education Director, AMSAT-NA
421 N. Military
Dearborn
M1 48124
USA

**NOAA:**
National Oceanic and Atmospheric Administration
US Department of Commerce
Rochville
Maryland 20852
USA

**Meteosat Programme:**
Eumetstat (Meteosat programme)
Am Elfengrund 45
61000 Darmstadt Eberstadt
Federal Republic of Germany

# Appendix 2

## SUPPLIERS

AMSAT-UK (Software for IBM, BBC, books, etc.)
94 Herongate Road
Wanstead Park
London E12 5EQ
Tel: 081-989 6741

Mr D. A. Duff
Research Manager
Unilab Limited
The Science Park
Hutton Street
Furthergate
Blackburn
BB1 3BT
Tel: 0254 681222

Mr R. Kirsch
Technical Services Manager
Maplin Electronics
Maplin Complex
Oak Road South
Benfleet
Essex SS7 2BB
Tel: 0702 554155

Mr P. Bennett
Head of Consumer Division
Cirkit
Park Lane
Broxbourne
Herts EN10 7NQ
Tel: 0992 441306

# Appendix 3

# FURTHER READING

1. *Communications Satellite Systems.* James Martin.
   Prentice-Hall Inc. 1978. £25.55.

2. *Observing Earth Satellites.* Desmond King-Hele.
   Macmillan. 1983. £9.95.

3. *Manual of Satellite Communications.* Emmanuel Fthenakis
   McGraw-Hill. 1984. £30.50.

4. *Satellites and Space Stations.* Moira Butterfield.
   Usborne. 1985. £2.50.

5. *Introducing Satellite Communications.* Bleazard.
   NCC Publications.

6. *Satellites in Education.* Craig Underwood.
   University of Surrey. £3.50 + £1 postage (from
   AMSAT-UK)

7. *Surrey University UoSAT. Spacecraft Data Booklet.*
   Unilab. Cat. No. 990.124. £3.95 (from AMSAT-UK)

8. *Guide to OSCAR Operating.* R.W.L. Limebear G3RWL.
   AMSAT-UK (updated, £3.50 + postage).

9. *UoSAT Microsatellites on ARIANE V35 ASAP.*
   Surrey Satellite Technology Limited. University of
   Surrey. 1990.

# Appendix 4
## LICENSING REQUIREMENTS

There is no specific licence required for receiving amateur satellite signals. In the case of radio amateurs using UoSATs/OSCARs for the transmission of messages and 'electronic mail' facilities they must have the appropriate amateur licence. Details of these requirements can be obtained from AMSAT-UK and also the Radio Society of Great Britain (RSGB).

A very detailed set of guidelines on how to conduct yourself as a licensed amateur when sending to a satellite is provided in 'Guide to Oscar Operating' (see Appendix 3).

There is no licence required for receiving weather satellite signals but the Department of Trade and Industry (DTI) do require users to obtain a letter of authority from them at no charge. This covers the NOAA and ESA series of satellites. The DTI address is:

> Room 309
> Radio Regulatory Division
> Waterloo Bridge House
> Waterloo Road
> London SE1 8UA.

Overseas readers are recommended to check with their own licensing authorities as to specific requirements.

# Index

*Notes*